THE ENCIRCLING HOP

A HISTORY OF HOPS
AND BREWING

THE ENCIRCLING HOP

A HISTORY OF HOPS AND BREWING

Margaret Lawrence

SAWD
England

By the same author

Peckham Pupils – The Development of
Education in a Kentish Village.

Through This Door – St. Michael's Church
East Peckham.

Remember East Peckham.

The New Church – Holy Trinity
East Peckham.

SAWD Publications
Placketts Hole, Bicknor,
Sittingbourne, Kent ME9 8BA.

British Library Cataloguing in Publication Data.
Lawrence. Margaret. *1931-*
The Encircling Hop: A History of Hops and Brewing.
1. Great Britain. Hops. Production. History
2. Great Britain. Brewing Industries, History
338.4766330941

ISBN: 1-872489-03-6

Copyright © 1990 Margaret Lawrence

Printed in Great Britain by Media Print, Sittingbourne, Kent.

Contents

Author's Preface

IT SEEMS STRANGE to be writing about hops and hop picking in Kent as past history because for hundreds of years and within living memory the county was the home of a thriving giant hop industry. This culture of the hop involved villagers all the year round and Londoners in their thousands in the September picking time.

Yet today in 1990 a whole generation of children have grown up without 'going hopping'. They don't know that in the last century many a headteacher gazed at an empty school in despair and wrote in the school log book:

> 'The school is empty. If the children are not hop picking they are looking after the baby while mother picks'.

They don't know that summer holidays were not primarily holidays but were arranged, after school attendance became compulsory, to allow children to be absent from school legally so that they could go to work in the hop gardens to help earn money for the family's winter clothing. Every pair of hands however small was vital.

Since the decline of the industry thousands of people have moved into Kent knowing nothing of the traditional industry and staring wide-eyed at their first sighting of 'a funny round building with a white thing on the top'. When this is explained as a vital feature of the Kentish hop industry and a much loved emblem in the county landscape their natural question is 'What are hops – why were they so special – when and where were they grown?'

It is necessary to tell the eager enquirer that the hop provides the major flavouring ingredient used in brewing beer. It is a plant which has always grown wild in Europe and Western Asia. Its botanical name is Humulus Lupulus and it belongs to the nettle family. The hop plant itself is a bine which can climb as high as 20 feet in a season. The hop bears male and female flowers on separate plants but it is the female flower which is used in brewing. It appears in July and matures through to September forming an elongated cone. Contained within the cone are many layers of petals which protect the seeds and, most important, the lupulin glands which provide the essential oils and resins.

But this botanical information does not convey the soul of the hop and how it has encircled the lives and outlook of Kentish people for centuries. Everyone who has had contact with hops knows that they are emotive; from the strange humming music of the wind playing on the hop garden wires to the whiff of the distinctive pungent smell rising suddenly and unexplainably from an old jacket in mid-winter; from the memories of early morning mists followed by long days of sunshine to the eager month by month watching the hop's progress in anticipation of the coming harvest. As one old lady said recently 'We just lived hops from one year's picking to the next'. How life was lived in a hopping community will be told through the story of one sample farm. It is not claimed that the experience of this farm is wholly representative. What is clear is that in order to be specific as to the details of life and work one living example communicates more than a mass of collated statistics.

Throughout the centuries the hop was close to the hopes and fears of ordinary people because it was used for medicinal purposes. Nicholas Culpeper the famous astrologer – physician of the early seventeenth century claimed that:

> 'The decoction of the tops (of the hops) cleanses the blood, cures the venereal desease, and all kinds of scabs, itch, and other breakings out of the body; as also tetters, ringworms, spreading sores and morphew, and all discolourings of the skin. The decoction of the flowers and tops help to expel poison. Half a dram of the seed in powder taken in drink kills worms in the body, brings down women's courses, and expels urine. A syrup made of the juice and sugar, cures the yellow jaundice, eases the headache that comes of heat, and tempers the heat of the liver and stomach, and is profitable given in long and hot agues that arrive from choler and blood. The young hop sprouts, which appear in March and April being mild, if boiled and served up

like asparagus are a very wholesome as well as a pleasant tasted spring food. They purify the blood and keep the body gently open'.

Belief in these remedies which used hops to relieve misery has long since faded but the real properties of the hop, imparting to beer its pleasurably sensual taste and its use as a preservative in brewing, had a lasting effect on the economic and social history of drinking for seven centuries and are of continuing relevance today. The answers to the enquirer's questions, Why? – When? – Where? lie in this long story.

Introducing
the Hop

NTIL THE THIRTEENTH century the common daily drink of Northern Europe was spiced ale. It was brewed with malt infused in water with the addition of some basic spices and was a heavy thick drink which after brewing had to be consumed quickly before it deteriorated. But in that century there was a great advance in large scale specialised brewing throughout Northern Europe. The main reason for the expansion was the introduction of hops in the brewing of beer.

One of the properties of the hop is its resinous constituents which have preservative effects, helping to produce a more durable, stable and palatable drink. Hops were cultivated in the Low Countries, (modern Belgium and Holland) on a growing scale from the thirteenth century long before they were cultivated in England. However by 1400 hopped ale was being imported into England and there is evidence from a Latin-English Dictionary published in 1440 'Promptorium Parvulorem' that hops had already been introduced into English brewing and four years later in the City of London surveyors of beer brewing were appointed as distinct from the ale brewers. The beer was made by skilled Flemish and Dutch brewers but there were many inexperienced Londoners who experimented with the new craft by simply adding hops to the traditional English ale and were prosecuted for the adulteration of ale.

The foreign brewers relied on imported hops because they do not appear to have been grown in England in any quantity at that time. It is thought that Flemish weavers may have introduced the crop on

1

a small scale to Kent, probably around Cranbrook, where they settled during the years after 1331 when Edward III had invited John Kemp of Ghent and his workers to settle in England to teach the English the art of weaving. It seems likely that people who had become used to hopped beer at home would have taken steps to obtain a drink felt to be so vital to their well being. But there were other immigrants from the continent who also contributed to small scale hop growing.

Little is known about this period but from the time of the arrival of religious refugees from Flanders (in the north of modern Belgium) in 1525 there is evidence of hop growing. But the skills belonged to the Flemish and payments were made by King Edward VI's Privy Council in 1549 for charges in bringing over hop setters, and twice in the following year to professionals like:

> 'Peter de Wolf and certain workmen under him for their wages...for planting and setting of hops'

and again two years later forty pounds were paid to him for:

> 'the planting of hops which he hath lately practiced within the realm'.

William Harrison, writing in 1577 described the new crop in his book 'Description of England'.

> 'Of late years we have found and taken up a great trade in planting hops, whereof our moorie and hitherto unprofitable grounds doo yield such plentie and increase, that there are few farmers who have not gardens and hops growing of their owne, and these far better than doo come from Flanders unto us'.

How accurate and reliable his description was cannot now be judged but it is clear that this was indeed a new crop. The fact that the English were leaning on the Flemish expertise is nowhere better explained than in a book published in 1574.

The writer says:

> Truly it grieveth me daily to see time ill spent, labour lost, cost cast away, much good ground naughtily applied and many good men shamefuly abused through ignorance and ignorant workmen that undertake to deal herein'.

They were in fact making fools of themselves because, as the writer continues:

> 'There is no reason why hoppes cannot be grown on English soil...I see the Flemings envy our practice herein who altogether

tend their own profit, seeking to empound us in the ignorance of our own commodities, to cram us with the wares and fruits of THEIR country and to do anything which might put impediment to this purpose, dazzling us with the discommendation of our soil, obscuring and falsifying the order of this mystery, sending us to Flanders as far as Poppering for that which we may find at home in our own back sides'.

The indignant author, whose name is synonymous with the hop industry, was Reynolde Scot. He set out to reform the English hop industry and succeeded. At a period when books were in the main only within the reach of the gentry his book was reprinted twice and read by yeomen farmers. His success lay in the fact that although as nephew of Sir Reynolde Scot he was of the county gentry, a Scot of Scott Hall; with inherited lands at Smeeth and Brabourne in East Kent, he could speak the language of the common man, the patois of the field and market place. Although he had enjoyed the gentleman's classical education at Oxford and was skilled in the tedious Art of Rhetoric he was willing to incur the danger of derision among his own class 'by speaking homely to those who have not been bought up in close study to decipher the Art of Rhetoric with their wits, but have been trained in the open fields to practise the Art of Husbandry with their lymmes (limbs)'. He said that he would write plainly to plain men of the country and that he would teach without great error or tediousness and 'you will learn, (I hope) without great payne or charges the manner howe, the time when and the place where to plant hops with effect'.

And so in his plain manner he set out his book: *A Perfite Platforme of a Hoppe Garden and necessary instructions for the making and maintenance thereof, with notes and rules for reformation of all abuses commonly practiced therein, very necessary and expedient for all men to have which in any wise have to do with hops'.*

The Market
for Hops

 ITH A FLOURISHING Flemish hop industry being challenged by the prospect of a flourishing, reformed, and inspired English hop industry the question naturally arises as to what was the market for hops?

Some enlightenment comes from a government survey of 1577 which shows that drinking houses at this period fell into three categories; inns, taverns and ale houses.

Inns, whose origin had been to provide only food and lodgings, had developed into elite establishments in the towns where their premises, often rebuilt or enlarged, dominated the main streets. They were fashionable centres offering wine, ale and beer with elaborate food and lodgings for the rich. They had also become commercial centres for merchants and traders. Local people from the upper classes used the inn to drink socially and to talk politics.

Taverns had originated as upper class drinking houses with the difference that their emphasis was on wine selling although beer was also readily sold. There was limited food and accommodation and they were meeting places for business.

Ale houses, known as Tippling Houses, the forerunners of the public house, were well established and were far more numerous than inns or taverns. Based on the government survey of 1577 to enquire 'what number of inns, taverns and ale houses are in every shire', it has been estimated that there were 24,000 ale house keepers in England as a whole. They were much smaller premises than inns or taverns serving ale or beer and providing only basic food and accommodation to the

5

lower classes which consisted of farmers, craftsmen, artisans, labourers and servants. They were an essential feature of the social life of ordinary people.

Ale houses had developed from the market stalls used in open air trading. Ale sellers increased in the fourteenth century when the number of new market centres reached 1,200. The ale sellers also sold ale from house to house but at that time the church and trade guilds provided accommodation and there had not been any incentive for the ale seller to make his house a social centre or any vision that he might do so.

Not all drink was sold through these channels. Many poor people bought their supplies at the ale house door filling buckets and barrels to take home for their daily needs. Craftsmen sent out for jugs of beer to drink while they worked. In addition many large houses brewed their own supplies for the household. The need was often enforced by the inadequacy of drinking water supplies. People had in the past used spring or river water but at this period such sources were becoming polluted in towns and areas affected by rural industries. The fact that beer had been boiled was a preventative against infection and this together with the nutritional value encouraged its use.

There was then a wide market of potential drinkers for those who chose to sell liquor. In Kent there was an additional market well known to Reynolde Scot in the need for hospitality for merchants and travellers of numerous description en route from London to the continent through Kent via Dover.

Another crucial question might be who was using the hops for brewing?

Ale brewing had been traditionally carried out by women, the ale wives. The process depended on natural changes in the materials which once they were initiated proceeded by themselves. It was an easy process and could be managed in the household and needed nothing more than primitive and cheap equipment in the form of a vessel made of copper for heating water over the open fire and some wooden casks (vats or tuns). While the water, (the liquor) was heating in the copper the ale wife mixed dried malt with quantities of unmalted grain. She then turned this into the mash vat to form the grist. She poured on some of the heated water and mixed it into the grist by hand leaving the remaining water to reach a higher temperature. She added that in stages raising the temperature with each addition until the starch in the mixture turned to sugar. She then separated the mash from the spent grains and turned it into cooling vessels. When the liquid (wort) was cooled it was poured into vats and yeast was added and left to ferment. After several days when secondary fermentation had taken place spices were added to what had become alcohol.

Because of its simplicity numerous poor people could turn to brewing and selling ale as a means of support. Because of ale's quick deterioration without preservatives only small quantities could be made at any one time and the ale seller was often out of drink. Another disadvantage had been that ingredients were not available in large quantities and supplies were irregular. Some poor brewers could only brew in harvest time when malt was easily available. But the change to brewing with hops required more vessels and more sophisticated equipment including a mash tun with a double bottom, and an enclosed furnace for lengthier boiling rather than an open fire. The longer boiling required much more wood which in some areas was in short supply. In equally short supply were the hops themselves which were also expensive as they were imported from the Netherlands. The small ale brewer found that he could not meet the demand for beer and moreover could not compete with the town based common brewers who moved quickly to exploit the new market for beer. He was forced to buy supplies from these urban brewers.

A vital clue to the success of hopped beer was that it was more economic to produce; a point to be considered at a time of rising costs. A bushel of malt produced only 8 gallons of ale but would yield 18 gallons of beer which enabled the producer to sell at a cheaper rate. Added to this was the unaccountable trend of fashion – it simply became fashionable to drink the clearer lighter and more palatable beer. There was also more choice of drink as the old spiced ale only came in two types – strong and small. Beer came in three varieties – strong, middle and small. The small beer was the daily domestic drink of the lower classes and was made by pouring a fresh volume of water over the wort in the vat after the strong beer had been drawn off. The beers were more potent than the old ale partly because the fermentation was more complete with the addition of hops but also because the higher yield of malt in beer brewing enabled the producers to increase the malt content of their grist and still make a profit.

Thus the market for hops was developed and there was an acceptance by all classes that hopped beer had come to stay. This market was for the English farmers to grasp and conquer in their own right rather than to continue to rely on the Flemish expertise. This was the market to which Reynolde Scot was pointing.

The Birth
of the English
Hop Industry

T IS CLEAR THAT farmers had previously attempted hop growing because as a true teacher Scot began his instructions with basics, warning the farmers that they must learn from their mistakes and

'be taught the reformation of many abuses which are received in most places as good rules'.

Then he lures his readers to read on with the promise of profit.

'There cannot lightly be employed grounde to more profitable use ,nor labour to more certayne gaynes,'

but having caught their ear he counters by showing them that it is not easy. There is much to consider.

First the farmer, with much thought, must choose the 'platforme' or site, of his hop garden considering the soil, choosing the heaviest ground which had proved to bear the most weight of hops. Hopefully they could avoid a site very open and bleak to the south because storms were frequent in late summer just at the time when the hops were most vulnerable. They needed lots of sunshine and protection from

'violence and contagion of the wind'.

Then they must use wisdom to consider the quantity which they can comfortably manage.

'Grow as much as and no more than you can dispose of and do not be lured by the desire for profit to cultivate hops to excess,'

This was obviously a mistake Scot had noticed and he advised them to aim small, –

'an acre of ground, and the third part of one man's labour, with small cost beside will yield unto him that ordereth well, forty marks yearly, and that for ever'.

Having dealt with their planning Scot goes on to advise how to set out and plant the hops. He must have seen hops planted higgledy piggledy because he advises the use of a pole or a line to get equal distances between the plants which would allow each one to get the sunshine and would allow the garden to be ploughed between the hills, whereas he had seen labour and money wasted on hand digging the gardens. He had also seen many different ways of planting hops but only recommended one, that of digging a hole one foot square and one foot deep and planting four plants in the centre close together, not one in each corner for this he considered wasted labour. Planting was to be done not later than April.

One essential thing a new hop grower needed to consider was the supply of wood for the hop poles. Some growers used four poles to a plant but it was possible to use only three which could keep down expense and from his observation of the Flemish practices at Poppering he remarked that they could plant alders on the north and east sides of their gardens and eventually be able to maintain themselves in poles. The essential thing was that they should be only 15 or 16 ft. long because if the hop climbed too high it became weak and thin.

The poles should be set in the ground 1½ft. deep, and erected at the time when the shoots appear above ground and set slightly inclining from one another. The hops should be tied to the poles with rushes or woollen material. The next process was forming the hills round each plant. These were mounds of earth formed like a sugar lump flattened on the top and standing about three feet high. The purpose was to beat the weeds and he had no complaint to make about the considerable labour which he said was needed continually until the time of picking. He did however complain about the abuses he had seen when

'many covetous men thinking (in haste) to enlarge their lucre do find (at leisure) their commodity diminished whyllst they make their hils so thick, their poles too long and suffer too many stalks to grow upon one pole'.

The main observation he made about the crucial picking was to make sure the hops were not wet and were picked quickly.

10

'For the speedier despatch thereof procure as much help as you can. . .neither make any delay of gathering after the time of cutting for in standing abroad they shall shed their seed wherein consisteth the chiefe vertue of the hoppe'.

He must have observed that after taking all care a grower could at that point lose the value of all he had worked for.

The book was illustrated with very clear woodcuts –

'to assist the understanding of the reader, especially those who could not read at all for whose sake the figures were made'.

His efforts to communicate were well rewarded because his book remained the standard work on hops for two hundred years and because of his advice on how to beat the Flemish at their own game there was an expansion of hop growing which has been called "The Birth of the English Hop Industry".

At first farmers in many counties tried to grow hops and there are even records of hop growing in Scotland and Wales but difficulties became apparent and eventually, even though small acreages were grown in some fourteen counties, Hereford, Worcester and Kent became the main hop growing areas with the latter soon establishing itself as the dominant producer.

Hops succeeded in Kent because the field system was suitable and convenient for experimenting with a new crop. Some regions of the country were farmed on the medieval open field system but Kent's agricultural system was historically different and the open field system was never operated there. It was a county of small enclosed fields suitable for Scot's recommendation of a small acreage of hops and they were well hedged for protection from the wind. The climate proved to be suitable and the county was well wooded and thus able to supply the thousands of poles required. The farmers also had the benefit of the fact that Flemish refugees with knowledge of hop culture had settled in Kent but the most important ingredient for success was that in some areas of the county a variety of soils proved to be suitable.

In spite of their advantages the Kentish hop grower grew a comparatively small acreage and could by no means meet the demand of the market. A large quantity of foreign hops continued to be imported, but not without challenge. It was found that great frauds by foreign merchants were a general practice. Many imported sacks were found to be falsely packed to include leaves, stalks, powder, sand, straw, lumps of wood and much soil thus increasing the weight of the hops sold to the advantage of the merchant. The government

11

considered that the country had been defrauded of at least £20,000 annually, a sum which gives some indication of the vast trade in hops. Fraud was not the only problem. It was also considered that there was a health hazard from the corrupt sacks which often contained only one third of good clean hops to two thirds of rubbish. To counteract this an Act of Parliament in 1603 decreed that in order to avoid sickness such hops were to be forfeited by the merchant and also by any English brewer found to be using them. Although the abuse was checked by examination of all sacks by one or more hop merchants later Acts of Parliament continued the pressure against fraudulent hops.

About this time ale houses became the subject of puritan disapproval. Preachers, government ministers, magistrates, village representatives and even neighbours joined in the attack and many attempts were made to reduce their number. A petition from the inhabitants of Yalding was presented to the Justices of the Peace at Quarter Sessions in 1596 asking them:

> 'to take it into their serious considerations the many alehouses which are in the poore towne of Yalding which is a poor town. It is no market town and but a very small thorouefaire. . .we have in that poor toune foure alehouses licenced and in some parts of the parish some which sell drinks unlicenced which is a great means for to bringe many wandering persones and vagabonds to the towne and by the means of having so many it doth cause diverse poore men to lie there and spend that which they have earned and their wifes and children wante it at home'.

At Goudhurst in 1606 the parishioners complained about

> 'the mysbehavyour and evyll lyfe of John Mace and his wife'.

From the number of people brought to court for keeping alehouses, five more at Goudhurst and six at Cranbrook to mention but a few, it is obvious that drinking in ale houses was wide spread.

On the same theme, in the neighbouring village of East Peckham, 'some old men', providing evidence in a tithe dispute, remembered that Sir Anthony Weldon, a strict puritan, had caused a house adjoining the churchyard wall to be pulled down because

> 'it gave disturbance by noise and tippling in the time of church service'.[1]

The size and importance of the brewing market using both home and imported hops was recognised by the Long Parliament in 1643 when it imposed the excise on beer and ale in anticipation that it would provide income for the war against the King. This caused some variation in demand but after the Restoration of the King the excise returns indicate that an average of three quarts of beer were drunk every week by every inhabitant. It is likely however that the true figure of consumption was higher because the excise did not include home brewed drink.

Much of the drinking took place in the inns which had continued to develop. There were extensions to old inns and there were those newly built with stabling for numerous horses. Continuing their role as commercial centres they had become important links in overland transport and were communication centres for the large number of commercial carriers. They became increasingly respectable as social centres for fashionable entertainment and were used for meetings of local government and for judicial purposes. After the Restoration there was an upsurge in coaching services for the upper classes with 900 coaches operating to London every week from all areas of the country using the inns as staging posts. Newspapers were distributed via the inns and the expanding Post Office also used inns as collecting and dropping points.

The greater part of hop supplies were still imported and it was not until 1690 that the government acted to use the assets of the drinking market for the benefit of the English hop growers. They improved and encouraged home production by placing a duty of 20 shillings per hundredweight over and above all other charges on imported hops.

The market was helped further by an Act of Parliament of 1710. When hops had been scarce some brewers had tried to use other ingredients to give the bitter taste to beer. Among others, they used pine and willow bark, cascarilla bark, quassia, gentian, colocynth, walnut leaf, wormwood bitter, extract of aloes, cocculus indicus berries, and capsicum. But the Act proclaimed:

> 'It is found by experience that hops used in the making of mält drinks are more wholesome for those who drink the same and of great advantage to the drink itself than any other bitter ingredient that can be used instead thereof and therefore no common brewer, inn keeper, or victualler is to use any broom, wormwood or any other bitter ingredient instead of hops in brewing any beer or ale which is intended for sale'.

This twofold action by the government was fortunate for the brewers because there were two important developments during the eighteenth century which had a great effect on the demand for hops.

The Porter
Years

HE PREVIOUS CHANGE to hopped beer had brought lasting social changes. The introduction of yet another new product was to have comparatively brief success but caused long-term development leading to the commercial organisation of the brewing industry. The range of beer available in London ale houses included stout butt beer which was the strongest beer on the market, strong brown ale, common brown ale, pale and amber beers (ale and beer were terms now both used to describe hopped liquor). A customer often asked for a drink mixed from two or more casks. One such mixture consisting of new and stale brown ales and pale ale, was known as three threads. But it was a slow process to draw beer from three casks for one customer and a partner in the Bell Brewhouse at Shoreditch thought of brewing one beer combining the merits of all three. The new beer was known as 'entire' because it was a compound drink drawn entirely from one cask. Because it was brewed from brown malts it was thick and dark. Its bitterness to the palate was the result of being more heavily hopped than the brown ales.

The new beer was immediately successful and became very popular with London labourers and porters and consequently became known as Porter. First brewed in 1722, in only four years it won a great proportion of the London market. Apart from the sheer taste it was popular because at 3d, it was a penny a quart cheaper than other beer.

Yet from the smaller brewer's point of view, production costs were higher; the porter had to be matured in casks for much longer than conventional beers. This required bigger stocks, a greater cellarage,

15

more cask and more labour. But at the same time, because porter was the first beer which was ideal for mass production, the bigger common brewers benefitted from economies of scale as their production increased. But it was a business which required massive capital investment. It was estimated that it required more capital than any other trade except banking. The large London brewers were able to expand dramatically while smaller brewers floundered and declined in number. Many of the modern brewing combines have their origins in the great porter breweries of this time. Most successful were Whitbread, Charrington and Moss, Courage and in Ireland, Guinness.

The trade in porter was lucrative. This fact was confirmed by Dr. Johnson who as an executor for the sale of Thrale's renowned brewery in 1781 said, 'We are not here to sell a parcel of boilers and vats, but the potentiality of growing rich beyond the dream of avarice'. With their profits the brewers bought freehold and leasehold properties which ensured outlets for their products. This was the beginning of the tied house system and future monopolies. They were also able to buy country estates and set themselves up as country gentlemen.

The sheer size of the enterprises was enormous. Before the appearance of porter no common brewer in London had grown to any extent, that is beyond the production of 5,000 barrels a year. By 1748 two brothers, the Calverts, who ran independent breweries, alone increased that output tenfold and produced 50,000 barrels. A century later six London porter brewers were producing over 100,000 barrels a year and Barclay Perkins, Whitbread and Meux Reid were brewing twice this amount. Brewing became a scientific operation and the great London brewers were as much a part of the Industrial Revolution as the heavy industries. Because they were pioneers in the new factory world, foreign visitors acclaimed their breweries to be among the industrial wonders of the kingdom.

Porter brewing spread throughout the country and made possible the rise of the major provincial brewers. Particular mention must be made of Burton-on-Trent whose very name came to be the standard against which all other beers were measured. Beneath the town were deposits of gypsum which gave the town a great reputation for the purity of its water, the most important ingredient in brewing and the one which gave individual flavour to local brews. It had been used since monastic days to produce enormous quantities of ale, the fame of which spread to the London market and eventually to a successful export trade with the Baltic. Among the earlier brewers to establish themselves, and who were to become national names, were Allsopp, Bass and Worthington. By the late Victorian period Burton contained thirty breweries which gave employment to 8,000 men and boys.

In Kent the emergence of potentially large scale brewers can be traced. The Gravesend brewery and the Rigden at Faversham were established in the early 1700s. The Phoenix Brewery at Dover was founded in 1740 as was the Cobb family brewery at Margate where there were other brewers because the town had 40 malt houses by 1772. A brewery was established at Tenterden in 1745, and at Rochester the Troy Town brewery was established in 1750, while at Lenham the Ash brewery was established in 1785. The Best Brewery at Chatham and the combined Upper and Lower Breweries in Maidstone both dating from the seventeenth century flourished at this period and at Canterbury, where six brewing aldermen supplying five or six score alehouses had been recorded in 1620, a similar number were operating. One brewer, Thomas Fenner formed a partnership with his son-in-law to form the famous business of Fenner and Flint in 1780. At Ramsgate the Tomson Brewery flourished after being purchased about 1680 as did the Hythe brewery established in 1699. No doubt many other breweries of this period remain undiscovered among town title deeds such as 'The Leasehold brewery and premises', leased 1797 in West Malling on the death of its previous owner.[2]

From the hop grower's point of view the enormous increase in brewing plus the fact that porter was more heavily hopped than beer meant an increase in the demand for hops, especially as those from Kent were found to be most suitable for the Burton products. The Kent growers rose to the market. They were strategically placed for supplying the London market, the East Kent growers exporting by sea from the coastal towns and the Mid-Kent farmers loading at Maidstone using the Medway.

Daniel Defoe in his Tour of 1724 noted that hops were being planted in abundance all over the county of Hereford but he was even more surprised at what he saw in Kent. Although there were hops in plenty around Maidstone it was around Canterbury that

'the most surprising increase of hop grounds'

had recently been made. He was informed that there were 6,000 acres of hop gardens within a very few miles of the city:

'the grounds in this part proving particularly fruitful for hops which was not at first known'.

17

Twenty years later a much travelled man, William Ellis wrote:

'There are many and greater plantations of hops made within these four years past more than ever before and many more like to be'.

Undoubtedly this increased activity was in response to the newly developed London market. At the beginning of the century when statistics first became available, there were 20,000 acres of hops in the country which increased by 15,000 during the century to 35,000. Although there were some reports of large acreages, the Kentish estate maps of that period show that most farmers grew a small acreage around their house as advised by Scot but as the demand grew those farmers with capital increased their acreages, and Hop Tithe records from the village of East Peckham show that 53 people were growing 558 acres, the amounts varying between half an acre and 49 acres.[3]

The stable price of porter was part of its popularity. At one period it remained unchanged for thirty years but its popularity was destroyed by heavy wartime rises in duty and inflated prices of raw materials after harvest failures. It rose by 2d a quart and some brewers began to economise by producing a paler porter which was not so popular. Other brewers economised by adulterating the liquor. They cut the alcohol content and replaced it with chemicals and other ingredients such as copperas, hartshorn shavings and opium. Although this reduced the price there were mass complaints to Parliament about the quality and there was a decline in demand.

Porter may have had a limited span of popularity but the customers and the hop growers were there to drink to another day. The long term effect on the brewing industry was that the large scale brewing companies had come to stay.

The Golden Age – and Beyond

N SPITE OF THE great increase in population there was a decline in the number of ale houses. The rate of population increase had accelerated from 1780. By 1801 England had 9.2 million inhabitants, 50% more than in 1750 and by 1831 this had risen to 13.9 million with the most spectacular growth in the new industrial cities, although there was not a rise in the number of drinking houses. The new poor of the industrial cities, afflicted by low incomes and bad living conditions, could afford nothing more than the barest necessities and in the countryside the increased population meant that the number of agricultural labourers was in excess of demand and there was large scale unemployment. But the main reason for the decline was a campaign against the ale houses, designed to reduce the number of licenced premises. In 1753 one ale house served the needs of 104 customers but by 1810 one ale house had to serve the needs of 350. The politicians saw them as rendezvous for political agitation, while the church leaders of the new evangelical movement saw them as places which needed reform. Any type of social disorder was blamed on the ale house.

From 1780 local measures were imposed by town councils and courts to restrict and regulate the licenced drink trade, and to curb popular drinking places and there was tight control over the issue of new licences. Because of restrictive licencing the big brewers took an unprecedented interest in gaining tied estates because they knew that they would have a virtual local monopoly. Because of the tight control gin shops became more numerous. Discontent over the licencing laws

19

led to much agitation and a Parliamentary Select Committee was set up to examine the retail drink trade. This resulted in the Beer Act of 1830 which liberalised the drink trade and allowed almost any householder to sell beer from his house as long as he obtained an excise licence costing £2. Opening times were restricted with keepers of inns, ale houses and victualling houses not allowed to open before 4 am or after 10 pm and they were to close during Divine Service. The monopoly of the brewers' tied houses was broken.

Up to this time ale houses had been ordinary dwelling houses but the freedom of the Beer Act encouraged brewers, builders and publicans to build premises specially designed as licenced premises, notably with cellars for storage, and by 1840 there were 15 per cent more public houses than in 1830. The number continued to grow until there were 69,000 in 1876. This time was known as the Golden Age of the Public House. It also gave rise to a massive development of the brewing industry.

Its magnitude is shown in a report drawn up in 1878 at the request of Mr. M.T. Bass, the member of Parliament for Derby and head of the greatest pale ale brewery in the world. It was shown that the total amount of capital invested in the liquor trades of the United Kingdom was about one hundred and seventeen million pounds sterling. The sum was equal to more than half the total value of the export trade and more than double the annual receipts of all the railways. About one third of the whole National Revenue was drawn from that source and the number of people directly employed in the various trades connected with the production and distribution of alcoholic drinks was one and a half million. Unfortunately there was another aspect to consider, that of wide-scale drunkenness leading to domestic misery for thousands.

Once again the hop growers catered for the burgeoning market. After only a gradual increase in the first half of the century, reflecting the decline in porter brewing and the decline in the number of ale houses, the acreage rose, and sharply, after 1862 (when the hop excise duty was removed) to 71,789 acres, in the peak year of 1878. Thus over a period of 78 years the hop acreage doubled and the second half of the century also became known as The Golden Age of the Hop Industry, matching that of the public house. As always the hop acreage was related to the current market.

It was a time of affluence for the farmers, with farmhouses being enlarged and surrounded by new farm yards with solid brick buildings. Ranges of new style roundel oasts for hop drying were now erected as more and more kilns were needed to cope with the demand.

At this point the picture becomes shadowed. From the peak of 1878 the hop industry began to falter and the situation was serious enough for a government enquiry in 1890. This concluded that the recession in acreage was due to a change in taste. Once again the unpredictable trend of fashion which had seen the advancement of hopped ale in the sixteenth century and of porter in the eighteenth had its repercussions on the hop industry. Porter was a dark, heavy, nutritious drink suitable for the working man but there had been a call from the hot climates of the British Empire for a less nutritious, brighter, lighter and more refreshing beer. Known as Indian Ale and Pale Ale, it was made with better quality hops. This made redundant the inferior hops which had been suitable for porter brewing and the gardens producing these were destroyed to the great loss of the grower. Moreover the larger growers who had capital could afford to go in for intensive cultivation and scientific experiment while the smaller had to sell out for less than the cost of production and many went bankrupt.

Another crisis was the renewed import of foreign hops which flooded the market and so threatened the industry that in 1908 the London and Provincial Hop Growers and Pickers Defence League organised the event known as Hop Saturday when growers and pickers alike demonstrated in Trafalgar Square to induce the government to impose a tariff on foreign hops. The event was preceded by mass demonstrations in Kent and photographs taken at the time emphasise the number of men involved in the industry. Although the tariff was imposed for a short time, a further crisis came in the First World War when the duty on a barrel of beer was trebled in the government's attempt to restrict socialising in order to concentrate the people's energy on the war effort. Unfortunately this also reduced the demand for hops from the brewers.

When the agreement on foreign hops terminated the growers formed a voluntary co-operative but when this too came to an end there was another crisis with the collapse of prices, less demand from the brewers, large acreages grubbed and great financial losses for the small growers. Added to this was an outbreak of hop diseases, disastrous weather conditions and the General Depression of the 1930s. Those who kept their nerve and had some capital to fall back on survived to take advantage of the formation of the Hop Marketing Board in 1932. With its headquarters at Paddock Wood, Kent this was the first statutory body under the Agricultural Marketing Act. It provided a closed market and stability for English hop growers and brewers because the Board would negotiate a guaranteed price with growers based on the estimated cost of production plus a 15% profit margin. The brewers would indicate their expected demand to the Board and each grower would be allocated a quota. Thus the hop acreage was controlled and losses for the farmer avoided.

But by then the damage to the industry was evident – the acreage had fallen to 11,000, almost half of the previous lowest figure ever recorded, those 20,000 acres quoted when figures first became available at the beginning of the eighteenth century.

Under the Board's rigid system of quotas to balance supply and demand the acreage rose to 13,000 over the next twenty-five years and slowly to 20,000 in 1968. By then the years had seen the almost complete mechanisation of the industry but in spite of these improvements a new crisis was looming for the hop industry.

Once again the unexplainable trend of fashion influenced the hop market. The more leisured young people, unused to the old heavy industrial work did not need the beers to quench their thirst, nor did they need the nutritional content because of improved dietary standards. Encouraged by brewers' advertising campaigns they began to experiment with new, unfamiliar drinks and in particular the new fashion for lager.

Lager is a beer which originated in Germany. It is brewed by using paler malt which gives the drink its characteristic light colour but the chief difference from English beers is that the time spent in fermentation is longer. Indeed the very word which turned the hop industry upside down in the mid-twentieth century means simply beer which has been kept in lagers or stores. The fashion for lager beer has been as revolutionary for the hop industry as the change to hopped ale in the thirteenth century and the introduction of porter in the eighteenth. The sales over twenty years have risen from 10 per cent of total beer sales to close on fifty per cent.

The attraction for the brewers was that the production was more profitable because they needed only two thirds of the hops required for brewing traditional English beers thus reducing their overheads. While this was problem enough for the growers in that it reduced the brewers' demands for hops, the main problem was that lager was thought to require seedless hops of the High Alpha category which were completely different from the seeded hops of the High Aroma category which the farmers had traditionally grown. To the growers' dismay they lost their market as the lager brewers began importing seedless hops from Germany, the home of lager.

Once again the growers responded to the market and planted High Alpha hops with success and although it was proved that lager can also be successfully brewed from the traditional English hop the Continental and North American lager manufacturers with subsidiaries in Britain continued using imported seedless hops. At the same time hop prices fell to an uneconomic level and many farmers were forced to grub their gardens. Many 'hop' villages are now devoid of hops with only the road names on new housing estates recording the names of hop varieties which once were familiar local words – Whitebine, Henham, Golding, Fuggles.

The result of the lager fashion has been the collapse of the old traditional hop industry. Another reason for reduced acreage was the scientific research and hop breeding programme at Kent's Wye College, the agricultural department of London University which has succeeded in achieving a higher yield from a smaller acreage.

After successfully controlling the hop market for fifty years the Hop Marketing Board was wound up in 1982 after the Treaty of Rome when England entered the European Economic Market. Monopoly organisations are not permitted within the Community and the Board was replaced in 1985 by English Hops Ltd. Their aim is to strengthen their marketing position in a fiercely competitive world market. They intend to return to the position of supplying the home brewing industry with one hundred per cent of hops and to aim for specific export markets to the Continent and America. They are a national voluntary co-operative with a dominant share in the market but the element of competition has been introduced and they now compete with four other similar co-operatives namely – Wealden Hops and Hop Sales Ltd., mainly in Kent and Sussex, Western Quality Hops and Hawk Brand East and West operating in Hereford and Worcester. Because of the voluntary nature individual farmers can if they wish use their own initiative to market their hops and brewers are free to buy their hops from whom they please.

Perhaps it is now easier to understand why the lives of Kentish people have been encircled by hops. The whole story seems to be one of reaction to the brewing market. For the future, the new competitive nature of the hop market and the internationally respected scientific research at Wye College will be vital in meeting the many challenges during the closing years of the twentieth century.

There were hops and growers, brewers and beer, profits and losses but none would have been possible without the London pickers, the 'hoppers' whose lives were also encircled by the hop. They knew nothing of statistics and the ups and downs of the market but it is they who colour and dominate the ethos of the hop industry.

'And far and near
With accent clear
The hop-picker's song salutes the glad ear;
The old and the young
Unite in the throng,
And echo re-echoes their jocund song,
The hop picking time is a time of glee,
So merrily, merrily now sing we;
For the bloom of the hop is the secret spell
Of the bright pale ale that we love so well;
So gather it quickly with tender care,
And off to the wagons the treasure bear'.

from 'The Curiosities of Ale and Beer'.

Hoppers' Social Conditions

NTIL MODERN FARMING with crop specialisation, the farmer grew his hops within the traditional pattern of mixed farming. What made the hops so special above other crops was not so much the acreage grown but the amount of help required to pick the hops in September when the value of the crop depended on their being picked quickly at the right moment.

The main help came from the poor and unemployed of London but pickers also came from as far away as Wales and Ireland and later from the new industrial towns in the north. The number increased after the Act of 1710 which increased the hop acreage and again in early Victorian years when the acreage rose to meet the demand from brewers in the new industrial towns. But at this point force met force. Up to 1834 the poor and unemployed and homeless had found shelter within their village workhouse, but the Poor Law Amendment Act of 1834 closed the local workhouses and provided instead the large Union Workhouses to which the poor from a group, or union, of parishes could be sent. The rules for entering these new establishments were very strict because they required complete separation of families and surrender of all personal possessions. This prevented the family from ever returning home and so many chose to endure their poverty rather than go into the workhouse. The resulting increased number of poor and unemployed, many of whom surged into Kent for the chance to earn some money at the hop picking came from long distances, quite unaware of the demands of the journey, walking, sleeping rough, arriving destitute and often unable to find work. They came in their thousands presenting a social problem which was largely ignored.

Writing in 1889, John Bickerdyke describes the people and the scene on the dusty highway as the hoppers poured into Kent. *'The Curiosities of Ale and Beer':*

'If the weather be but reasonably fine, the life of these latter day pilgrims is not a hard one for the balmy country air, the soft turf and beautiful surroundings must seem to these poor creatures a kind of paradise after the dens of filth, disease and darkness from which they have come. Not pleasant company are these pilgrims. As a rule they are uncleanly, their habits course, their language foul and their morality doubtful. Many persons in Kent prefer to lose several pounds rather than let their children go into the fields and associate with the mixed company from the East End. Poor people! They are after all what their circumstances have made them; a sweep can hardly be blamed for having a black face.

The high road from London to the hopfields of Kent presents a curious appearance immediately before the hop picking season. A stranger might imagine that the poorer classes of a big city were flying before an invading army. Grey haired, decrepit old men and women are to be seen painfully crawling along, their stronger sons and daughters pressing on impatiently. Children by the dozen, some fresh and leaping for joy at the green fields and sunshine, others crying from fatigue for the road is long and dusty. Nearly all the people carry sacks or baskets, or bundles, and some even push hand carts laden with clothing, rags, and odds and ends. Most of these folk are careless, merry people and beguile the way with many coarse jest, but here and there will be some hang-dog, bloated-faced ruffian tramping doggedly along, a discontented weary woman dragging slowly a few yards in his rear and as like as not carrying a half-starved sickly child in her shawl. . .Towards evening the pickers cease their tramp, and take up their quarters for the night in woodland copse, or under hedgerow or sheltering bank. Baskets, sacks, and handcarts are unpacked and here and there will be seen a whole family seated around a blazing wood fire over which boils the family kettle. Others less fortunate in having no family circle to join, betake themselves to more secluded quarters to munch the lump of bread of which their supper consists'.

How did the county cope with more than eighty thousand people pouring into Kent for several weeks each autumn? Very little was provided for them. The pickers were entitled to ask for accommodation at the Union Workhouses which reported horrifying over crowding and it was not until the last quarter of the nineteenth century that religious philanthropists began to bring to public notice the deplorable conditions faced by the hoppers.

The earliest worker was the Rev. J.J. Kendon, Vicar of Goudhurst (1860). More well known perhaps because of the Hoppers' Hospital he founded at Five Oak Green in 1910, was Father Richard Wilson, Vicar of St. Augustines, Stephney, who followed his parishioners to see where they went each summer and found most desperate human need in the hop gardens.

But of most particular interest to Beltring Farm, Paddock Wood, later to become Whitbread the brewers' Hop Farm, is the Franciscan Mission for Catholic Hop pickers. It was in 1905 that the new Roman Catholic Bishop of Southwark, Peter Amigo, wrote to the Capuchin Friars (a branch of the Franciscan Order) asking if anything could be done about the hop pickers who crowded into Kent in the summer.[4] There were Church of England and many nonconformist workers offering social and spiritual help to them but nothing was being done for the large number of Roman Catholics whose number was estimated at between eight and ten thousand. He said that he was thinking mainly about the East Farleigh and Paddock Wood areas both of which were nine miles from a Roman Catholic church. As a result of this concern Friar Cuthbert was sent to conduct the first mission to Catholic hop pickers.

In his report at the end of the first season Friar Cuthbert emphasised conditions which were appalling in their wretchedness and moral danger. He wrote that nothing in the conditions of the medieval peasantry could be worse than what he witnessed in the field. Pickers were herded at night into huts hardly better than pigsties, or into tents – twenty into tents only intended for six people – and moreover they were often of different families and sexes. Sometimes the accommodation was not even a hut or a tent but shelters made of sacking which made existence pitiable in wet weather. However, he continued, growers were clearly endeavouring to better the conditions and that this could be done was evident from what had been accomplished by the more humane growers over the previous ten years. The district had been a regular hell during the season but this year there had been comparative sobriety and orderliness and Saturday evenings had been no worse than the London streets. Various people assured the Friars that the improvement was chiefly owing to the influence of the missions run by the Anglican Church, the Salvation Army and other dissenting agencies who had brought nurses and coffee stalls and generally humanised conditions. As well as social and philanthropic work the missions had also attempted spiritual uplifting by means of lantern lectures on the life of Christ which were always well attended, but as yet nothing had been done for the spiritual needs of the eight to ten thousand Roman Catholics.

At East Farleigh and Wateringbury the Friars were not welcomed either by the local people or the hoppers. In particular, at Wateringbury the Church of England ran a very efficient mission including a hoppers' hospital and although they were accustomed to the church mission workers they viewed the Friars with suspicion, dressed as they were in their long brown robes. They even found accommodation difficult to find in these villages except at Paddock Wood. There Friar Cuthbert obtained permission from the principal hop grower for the mission to set its headquarters on the largest farm in the area and from there he was able to organise a system of social and religious work which spread out to other farms in the district.

The principal hop grower who had befriended the mission was E.A. White of Beltring Farm and Friar Cuthbert was fortunate to find that the appalling conditions which he had seen on other farms did not exist there. Although he did not describe the conditions himself, they were soon to be literally published abroad because in 1907 the farm was visited by Dr. Reginald Farrers, who, on the instructions of the Local Government Board, was making a report on *'The Lodgings and Accommodation of Hop pickers and Pickers of Fruit and Vegetables'*.[5]

His report published by Her Majesty's Stationery office said that he had visited farms in Kent, Sussex, Worcestershire Herefordshire, Essex and Hertfordshire and from this wide area he selected two groups of huts:

'for particular descriptions as illustrative types of excellent lodgings, which on farms where hops are grown regularly, may be provided for hop pickers at moderate cost'.

One farm was the Eardiston Farming Company in Worcestershire and the other was Beltring Farm, Paddock Wood, Kent.

But before giving his particular description of Beltring Farm the inspector described the general conditions he had found during his tour of inspection.

He found that accommodation was provided in various ways in ordinary farm buildings, such as barns, lofts, cartsheds, stables, cowsheds, tents and specially constructed huts. The farm buildings were generally found to be satisfactory and in Kent were usually divided by partitions into cubicles for the separate use of married couples and their families. The partitions were usually made of matchboarding, of sacking, or of hurdles covered with straw. The provision of separate cubicles was considered desirable in the interest of decency, although it added to the difficulties of ventilation. Sheep hurdles with the long bars placed horizontally without covering or sacking or straw were not considered an effective screen.

Tents were the most unsatisfactory accommodation, being very often in various stages of disrepair, often very badly stitched together, full of gaps and holes, which made for great misery in wet weather. But even tents in good repair gave rise to the evils of lack of privacy and he recommended that they should be confined to persons of the same sex or members of the same family,

> 'I found a large number of instances of improper accommodation of unrelated persons of different sexes in the same tent; in one case two married women without their husbands, two single young men, a girl of eighteen and six children occupied the same bell tent, none of the adults being related to each other'.

In describing the huts he wrote that the greater number of pickers in Kent were lodged in huts varying in size between 6ft. x 8ft. and 10ft. x 15ft. Height to eaves was generally 5ft. 9ins. The most common type of building material was wood with a corrugated iron roof and earth floor. Special openings were provided in various ways for lighting and ventilation, the door cut down or scalloped a few inches from the top, or latticed wooden openings. Where there were no special openings the regular apertures of the corrugated iron at the top of the wall provided light and ventilation.

As regards over crowding the farm buildings were least disturbing but in the tents he found gross and indecent over crowding, while huts were commonly over crowded. An average hut of 64 square feet was suitable for four adults and two or four children under ten years old but as families disliked to be separated, it was common to find two or more children over ten years old sharing with their parents as well as the younger children.

He also considered various other facilities offered to the pickers. Whereas in some instances he found no cooking shelters provided, they were provided on most farms and varied from adapted cart sheds or other farm buildings to specially built brick structures. In between there were sometimes mere corrugated roofs supported by uprights with or without walls. The absence of proper cooking and drying facilities in wet weather made the conditions of the pickers wretched.

He found grave objections to the mode of water supply. On several farms the water was delivered in open tanks of galvanised iron which exposed the water to the heat of the sun and to dirt and dust, and it was found particularly impossible to stop the children from dabbling in the water, washing their hands, even their feet in it and sometimes actually bathing in it. On another farm the pickers were obliged to use a tank also used by cattle, while some could only obtain water from foul running streams, or contaminated with sewerage, even from shallow ponds. However, in most farms he found a good supply of water, especially in that district of Kent, within the area of the Mid Kent Water Company's service.

Quite as serious were his findings about privy accommodation. In numerous instances he found none provided at all, and although on the majority of farms some kind was provided,

> 'The cases in which a sufficient number of suitable privies properly constructed, for the separate use of each sex, had been provided were on the whole the exception rather than the rule. In most cases the privies for men and women were closely adjoining and often not differentiated or were so constructed as not to allow of due privacy. The closet seats were often allowed to be in an extremely filthy condition and the privy pit was seldom filled in with earth'.

Also generally speaking he found an entire absence of any attempt at waste collection, the neighbourhood of the hop pickers' quarters being as a rule freely littered with refuse, food and other rubbish.

It was therefore with some pride that Beltring Farm received the inspector's comments.

Beltring Farm – Paddock Wood

LODGINGS WERE PROVIDED at Beltring for the pickers of 140 acres of hops. Accommodation was provided in twenty-four buildings and forty-six tents. Each building was divided into six double compartments entered by separate doors. A double compartment had an upstairs and downstairs chamber, the former being approached by a step ladder. The area of each hut was 10ft. x 8ft. 6ins; the height of the ground floor hut was 6ft. 6ins, and of the upstairs hut 4ft. to the eaves and 11ft. to the pitch of the roof. In general each hut accommodated a single family, but to some larger families double huts were assigned. It was reckoned that the twenty-four buildings would accommodate about 250 families. Other accommodation was provided in tents.

Fourteen of the huts were made of tarred wood with corrugated iron roofs. Ventilation was provided by a ventilator over each door and the frame of each door was raised a few inches above the ground. Flooring on the ground floor huts was of beaten earth and the upper of wood. There were no bedsteads but a plentiful layer of dry hop bines were provided on which straw was laid. 'An elastic and comfortable bed is thus provided'. It was thought however that an improvement could be made by providing end wooden lattice frames a few inches off the ground.

Another asset was the double cookhouses adjacent to each building, built of brick and with a corrugated iron roof and having six fireplaces back to back with three chimneys. Thus two families had the use of one fireplace to cook their food, and, a great advantage, to dry their clothes, instead of sleeping in them wet as described by other hoppers.

There was also ample privy accommodation. They were built out at the back of the wall of each cookhouse and had separate entrances for men and women. The privies were pits, having a wooden rail for the seat; they were regularly attended to, being treated three times a week with ashes and on Saturdays with lime and carbolic powder.

The farm scored on yet two more points. Here there was an ample pure water supply from four pumps and two standpipes, the latter being connected to the Mid Kent Water Company.

Only on the two farms selected was there any regular waste collection and on Beltring farm a baillif was employed to organise this and to keep order generally. The paths were strewn with quassia chips, a night watchman was employed to guard against fire and a medical practitioner was contracted to attend to the pickers in case of illness.

Mr. White kindly supplied the inspector with the cost of the brick buildings which he had so much admired.

Hopper-house (12 huts). £74.12s.2d
Cook-house £35.0s.0d
Closets £8.17s.10d
Total: £118.10s.0d

The cost of each hut was therefore £9.17.0d. including cooking and privy accommodation and this price was considered as 'very moderate, considering the permanency of the buildings and the comfort and conveniences afforded the pickers'.

And so while thousands of contemporary pickers were subject to many humiliating indecencies, Mr. White provided what for the age were palaces for his pickers, and not even he, or the inspector, could have foreseen them through the eyes of a future Local Authority as overcrowded, unventilated and insanitary. But for the hoppers, if the huts were windowless and stiflingly hot under a tin roof, there was plenty of fresh air outside and if flies from the open cess-pits flew round the corner to the cook house, was a country fly any worse than a London fly? Nothing, whatever the conditions, could inhibit their enthusiasm for their chance of a working holiday in the fresh air, getting out of dirty, smoke filled London – a London which has since been very much forgotten now that we live in the age of smokeless zones.

Taking a below average figure of six in each of the two hundred and fifty families who lived in the huts and in the forty-six tents a picture of 1,776 hoppers can be visualised on Bell Common and Tent Common but the true figure was probably much higher.

Thousands of these hoppers had already, for many years, been coming into Kent on special hopper trains. Writing at the same period as Mr. White built his huts, John Bickerdyke explains that about half the pickers used the trains to get to Kent but those who could not afford the fare walked and used some of their earnings for the fare home:

> 'Everything then is the height of merriment, and of such an uproarious kind as the people of the East End delight in. Young men and girls invigorated by their sojourn in the bracing country air, alike garland themselves with hops and decorate themselves with gay ribbons. Laughing, dancing, singing, they hurry to the station, or along the road to London. Practical jokes are played by the score, the railway officials are distracted, the police look the other way!'

The largest number that he had been able to trace in the railway records for the journey home was 19,000 in the years before 1882.

Another later description of 1913 is given by a Kent Messenger reporter at London Bridge station. The date is immaterial for the scene was an established tradition. He described how during the early hours of the morning three thousand hoppers had been despatched between the hours of twelve and three o'clock but long before the trains were due to leave the approach to the station had been choked with a miscellaneous crowd who sat in the gutter and reclined against the wall. From the corner of Tooley Street right up to the main line booking office the hoppers squatted in rows surrounded by their baggage waiting patiently to be shepherded to the special trains which were to convey them into Kent. The station office had prepared for the siege and had erected wooden posts dividing one of the entrances into two portions. Around them stood nearly two dozen ticket inspectors who did their best to get the travellers to line up evenly . He saw fathers carrying their families' luggage in sacks upon their heads and he had never seen so many prams put to so many uses, for every family seemed to have a baby and every baby had a pram or a mail cart and every one had a parcel strapped to where the baby should have been. The mite bore the strain and excitement with philosophical calm staring with big round eyes at the noisy, good natured crowd till their little heads dropped with exhaustion. At the end of Tooley Street the reporter saw some of the bolder hoppers organising an impromptu dance on the pavement to the accompaniment of a mouth organ. When they were not dancing they ate oysters bought from a barrow. To the hoppers' credit he remarked that there was good behaviour everywhere.

Those who travelled to Beltring left the train at Paddock Wood and finished their journey, some on foot pushing their prams and carts and some by farm wagon. The cost paid by Mr. White for the welcoming huts was small indeed for they helped to earn him an enduring reputation which is still respected in the district nearly seventy years after his death.

remayne vpon the vppermoſt ioynt thereof.

And when
you haue thus
done , preſſe
downe the
Earthe wyth
your foote hard
to the rootes ,
not treadinge
vppon them ,
but dryuinge
the loſe earth cloſe to the corner where the
rootes are ſette.

And here is to be noted, that the readyeſt and
eueneſt waye, is alwayes to ſet your rootes at
one certayne corner of the hole , which corner
ſhoulde alwayes be right vnderneath the ſayde
pinne or threde, as is afoze ſhewed.

At this time you muſt make no hill at all, but
onely couer the toppes of your rootes about two
ynches thick, with the fineſt moulde you can get.

When you
are driuen to
ſet your rootes
late, if there be
anye greene
ſprynges vpon
them, you may
take the ad=
uantage there=
of , leauynge
the

of a Hoppegarden

If you laye ſofte greene Buſhes abroade in
the deawe and in the Sunne , within two or three
dayes, they will be lythe, tough, and handſome
for this purpoſe of tying, which may not be fore=
boured, for it is moſt certaine that the Hoppe that
lyeth long vpon the grounde before he be tyed to
the Poale, proſpereth nothing ſo wel as it, which
ſoner attayneth therevnto.

¶ Of ſetting and byllis.

NOwe you muſt begyn to make your hils,
and for the better doing thereof, you muſt
prepare a toole of Iron faſhioned ſome=
what like to a Coopers Addes , but not ſo much
boowing, and therefore lykeſt to the netherpart of   This toole is
    here aboue
    better pro=
    portioned.

*Reynolde Scot's illustrations made especially to help those
farmers who could not read.*

In Kent mass demonstrations against foreign hops preceded the Hop Saturday demonstration in Trafalgar Square, 1908. Protesters at Tenterden.

Kent History Centre

An old print 'Hop-pickers on the road.'

(Drawn by "Phiz.")

Hoppers cooking in the open air before cook houses were provided.

Temporary dwellings for hop pickers before huts were built. c. 1870.

Kent History Centre

Picking in the rain – but there was no provision for drying clothes – Victorian artist's impression.

E.A. White gradually built huts to replace tents.

A London family enjoying their working holiday in the countryside.

The privies were at the back of the cooking shed wall.

Plan Section and Elevation of Hop-pickers Houses & Cook Houses.

Built on the Estate of Messrs. E. A. White Ltd.

Beltring, Paddock Wood. Kent.

SCALE ⅛" = 1 FOOT

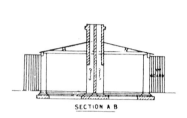

SECTION A B

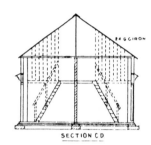

24 G IRON

SECTION C D

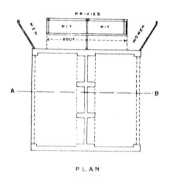

PRIVIES

MEN

PIT PIT

ROOF

WOMEN

A ———— B

PLAN

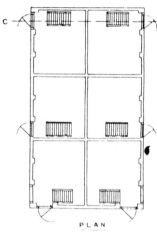

C

PLAN

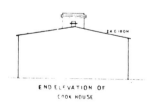

24 G IRON

END ELEVATION OF
COOK HOUSE

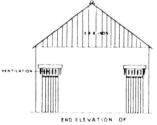

24 G IRON

VENTILATION

END ELEVATION OF
HOP PICKER HOUSES

Londoners arriving at Faversham Station. A typical scene throughout Kent.

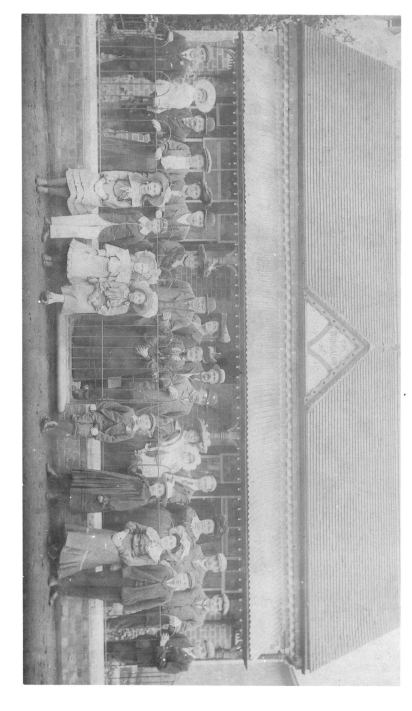

Mr. Thomas Webb and wife (centre) with their large family. He was responsible for building the famous Bell Oasts.

P. Skinner

An early picture of E.A. White's impressive oast houses built before 1894.

NON-ISONOUS "SPIMO" NON-POISONOUS
HOP AND FRUIT TREE WASH

Destroys Aphis Fly, Red Spider, Caterpillars, Maggots, Weavils, Mildew, etc.

PRAY FRUIT TREES just before fruit-buds open, and again when fruit is set.

IT PAYS TO DO IT,

TRY IT THIS SEASON.

"SPIMO" is a Complete Wash, ready at a moments notice. Full particulars, post free.

Manufactured and used by

E A. WHITE, LTD.,
HOP AND FRUIT GROWERS, BELTRING
PADDOCK WOOD, KENT.

E.A. White's new venture into insecticides was very successful.

Edward Albert White (1844-1922)

DWARD ALBERT WHITE became a legend. He was certainly one of those more enlightened hop growers referred to by Friar Cuthbert who had bettered the conditions of the pickers over the previous ten years because his new huts had been built before 1894, being included in the survey carried out at that date for the second edition of the Ordnance Survey Map.

He came from a local family of well-known gentlemen farmers and was born at Court Lodge, Yalding, in 1844, the son of Alfred and Anne White. His father Alfred, with his two brothers, Samuel and Thomas, had not only inherited considerably through the will of their father, Samuel White, Gentleman of Yalding, (1837) but also through their mother's family, being the major beneficiaries in the will of her brother, Lawrence Starnes, Gentleman of Yalding (1843). Edward certainly knew the advantages of the proverbial silver spoon.[6]

Being born a gentleman he was sent to Marlborough College for a gentleman's education and spent most of his teenage years there, between the ages of 13 and 17.[7] Although there is no record there of his sporting interests he did in fact come from a strong cricketing family. When his uncle, Thomas White heard that his local team at West Malling known as Town Malling was going to have to quit their ground he simply bought the farm on which the ground lay and gave instructions for enlarging the ground 'to annex to it so much as might be necessary for the purpose of the game'.

Edward himself became a well known Kent cricketer and between the years 1867 and 1875 played for the county twenty-nine times and was said to have been a good hitter and to have a strong defence. His highest score for the county was 81 at Canterbury in 1871 but his highest score of 96 was made while playing for the Gentlemen of Kent against the Gentlemen of Sussex at Brighton.[8]

But although he had the life style of a gentleman he is rather remembered as a true gentleman of heart whose main concern was for the welfare of his pickers. As well as the good accommodation, he aimed at making the camps self-sufficient so that everything could be bought from the camp shops to prevent the pickers being tempted to spend their money in the pubs if they went out shopping. Entertainment was also provided with the same aim in view. He shared his skill and love of sport with them and organised athletics – races for men and women, boys and girls and even baby crawling races. Every event had its prize. There were also three concerts a week, and a gramophone to keep the children amused. So concerned was he for these people whose health relied on these weeks in the countryside away from the smoke and fog of the towns that he was personally influential in organising 'Hop Saturday'. He was President of The London and Provincial Hop Growers and Pickers' Defence League because he knew that if the foreign hops took over the market the pickers would not be needed and their health and spirits would be damaged.

Mr. White farmed at Beltring for about fifty years and during that time he was responsible for a revolution in farming and became one of the greatest authorities in the farming world. He experimented with the scientific enterprise of cross-breeding by growing hop plants from seed in which field he was said to be a genius, and succeeded in producing a variety of hops which would ripen in sucessive weeks so that the season could be controlled. His results were proudly marketed as White's Goldings and his success can be seen by the awards shown on the hop pocket (see front cover) proudly held by the great man himself. This photograph was given by Mr. White to his secretary in whose family it has remained.

He worked in close liason with Professor Salmon who in time became known as 'the great Professor Salmon' at the newly formed Wye College, (University of London) which gives some indication of the scientific standards to which Mr. White was working.

He also foresaw that to cope with the success of being able to grow more hops by expanding the season he would need more oasts. Those he already had, which will be described later, were efficient enough for the old style standard of growing but they were not sufficient for the enterprise he had in mind. Therefore he approached Mr. Thomas Webb, a well-known and respected local builder of Bush House, Bullen Lane, East Peckham and later of The Freehold, East Peckham, concerning his plans for a whole range of new oasts. What Mr. Webb heard caused him to go to Mr. S. Wood, Builder, of the Apple Tree Public House, Orchard Road, East Peckham to ask him to consider helping with such a big project. Mr. Wood of Old Kent Road, Paddock Wood, recalls how his grandfather told the story and Mrs. Couttes-Smith, now living in Scotland, recalls that her grandfather, Thomas Webb employed her father, Mr. Ernest Norton, born 1878 as an apprentice on the oasts. Mr. Norton later married one of Mr. Webb's fourteen children, her mother.

By 1894 the range of four oasts with twenty cowls piercing the sky like banners in a medieval pageant were completed and in time for Mr. White's next big venture, because in 1894 he formed a limited company in order to raise more money for his enterprises. To do this he had to sell to the new Company all the lands which he had purchased. These were Brookers Farm, 122 acres, Lilly Hoo Farm, 83 acres, the Whettenhall estate, 94 acres, and Monktons, 14 acres (see map). He also had to sell his interest in the lease of Beltring Farm, 100 acres which he leased from the Drapers' Company in the City of London, making a total of 414 acres. Other assets taken over by the new company were, 'every description of property now belonging' which included strange new words in the farming world, 'Plant Machinery', but words which were to become vital.

As a result of these arrangements he was allotted £2,000 capital. The aims of the company as set out at its formation shows the range of farming activities carried on by Mr. White:

'To carry on all or any of the business in all or any of their branches, mainly hop planting and growing, farming, dairy farming, fruit and vegetable growing, market and nursery gardening, manufacture of provisions of all kinds, whether animal, vegetable or otherwise, forestry, charcoal burning, breeding of horses and cattle, and other live stock, dealing in hops, hop sets, fruit and other plant washes, or materials for making washes, horses, cattle and other livestock, and in all manner of farm, dairy, orchard, or nursery produce and implements, utensils and appliances, requisites and materials connected therewith or which may seem capable of being profitable'.[9]

Here again were strange new words intruding into the farming world; first there was 'plant machinery', and now, 'fruit and other plant washes'. The secret was that Mr. White was the pioneer of insecticides.

One of the problems with hop growing were the many diseases which affected the crop causing big losses to the growers. Mr. White invented a wash for his own use and invented an underground pipe system to take the washes to the hop gardens and consequently found that his crops were cleaner and much healthier. He also experimented with fruit tree washes with the same success; the hop washes he called Spimo and the fruit tree washes Abol. In fact he was so successful that he needed more capital to invest and explained to his shareholders in 1908 when raising money for the third time, that when the company was first formed, the insecticide business was small and the money subscribed practically all available for hop growing, whereas the insecticide part of the business had grown considerably absorbing a considerable amount of capital.

The business continued to grow with the company balance sheets between 1908 and 1918 indicating that the wash business far outstripped the farm business. It was pointed out by Mr. White that this was a far more stable business, unaffected by the weather whereas the hop industry was of a fluctuating character affected by the weather and other problems. However towards his closing years at the farm, 1917 and 1918, both businesses reached their peak.[10]

One of the ingredients of the washes was the bitter extract from the wood of the Quassia tree, which was imported from Jamaica in large logs. It was then reduced to more manageable pieces known as quassia chips, being about 1 x 4 x 9 inch thick. When the extract was exhausted the hardness of the wood still had a use in the economy of the farm being used to strew the paths around the hopper huts as observed by the inspector in his report. Whether they were anything more than just economical paving although in itself revolutionary, or whether they still contained some effective insecticide against the flies and gnats is not known.

This pioneer work in insecticides is remembered with great respect. When the company was wound up in 1920, a special resolution was drafted for the sale of the wash business and assets to Messrs. Abol Ltd., the forerunner of I.C.I. at Yalding.[11] The building used in the wash enterprise was demolished in 1983 but is given a permanent record on the 1908 Ordnance Survey Map, the barn being marked, 'Spimo factory.'

In his personal life Edward White married in 1873 when he was 29 years old. His bride, Mary Filder, was a widow of his own age and brought with her to Beltring a young family of three begun when she was eighteen years old. She was also a wealthy heiress owning property in Eastbourne, Tunbridge Wells, Northfleet, Middlesex, Surrey and Sussex, but her wealth was put into a trust fund for her children and was not available to her husband for his farming enterprises. She died aged 51 in 1895 leaving her own children, and Nellie, the only child of their marriage.[12]

Mr. White continued to farm at Beltring until he retired in 1919 having spent a life time in farming. He died in 1922 aged 78 years, when his address was given as Chiswick but it is remembered locally that his hearse was drawn around East Peckham on May 8th before he was interred in the White family vault at Yalding church, attended by forty old employees from Beltring.

While his world famous oasts remain as his monument the last word here is given to his hoppers:-

An old girl who regularly went hopping down at Whites
To earn a little for a rainy day,
Is growing old and feeble, and the other day she wrote
This letter as she on her death bed lay –
She wrote it to her daughter, who comes down every year,
In fact she first came when quite a babe,
Now she herself is married and got kiddies of her own,
Just listen now to what the letter said –

'Is the old farm in the same place? Are the same old pickers
                                                still about?
Does Mr. Grimes still put the tents up?
Does Darkie run about and shout?
Do the same old garden walkers blow their horns?
The same old bookies give you subs?
And does dear Mr. White give you concerts there at night
Just to keep you out of mischief and the pubs?

And now the hoppings all over and you're going back to town,
You'll not forget the sights you saw down here –
The gramophone and conjuring and George our first rate clown,
And Professor Vane whose turns we always cheer;
What with singing and with dancing and with many bright eyes
                                                glancing,
With shouts of 'Oh my darling' fill the air;

39

Folks can see it all gives pleasure and your hearts will doubtless tremble
Grateful memories of hopping-down in Kent.

Yes the old farm's in the same place and the dear old Guvnor's still about,
We've still got a Waite, but he doesn't Harris us,
And Darkie doesn't loose a chance to shout!
We've still got Pellat, Butchers, Wood, and Grimes,
Sweeting, King, and Guest as well as Knight;
We've a Waghorn and a Graph'horn that together do their best,
So Hip! Hooray ! Three cheers for E.A. White!

(Sung by Professor Vane at Beltring Entertainments, Paddock Wood, to the tune of 'Is the Old Home in the Same Place?' 1907).
from 'The Months of the Year' by Pemberton Lloyd.

John Herbert Waghorn (1883-1956)

EA. WHITE'S RETIREMENT from farming had presented Whitbread's Brewery with a problem. For many years they had taken Beltring hops and relied particularly on the flavour of the White's Golding for the continuity of the flavour of their beers and with a change of farmer they feared that they might lose their vital ingredient. They therefore made advances to E.A. White and Company for the purchase of their company and on December 12th, 1919 the Company passed a Special Resolution that:

> 'For the sale of The Company to Messrs. Whitbread and Co. Ltd.
> it is desirable to wind up this Company and accordingly that this
> Company be wound up voluntarily under the Companies Act of
> 1906'.

The liquidation was due to date from 1st January, 1920 but Whitbread had another problem because they could not buy Beltring Farm itself as it was owned by the Drapers' Company in the City of London. It had been entrusted to them in 1575 by William Lambarde, the Kentish notary, with the rent from the lease of the farm to provide income for the Queen Elizabeth Almshouses at Greenwich which he had founded. At this point however the Drapers' Company became willing to sell Beltring and after negotiations with the Charity Commissioners, sold Beltring farm to Whitbread for £8,000 – the first time it had changed hands for 345 years. The conveyance was signed on 11th August 1920.[13]

The takeover and the general running of the farm was made easier by the personality and ability of one man who was to become as much a legend as his master before him. John Herbert Waghorn was baptised at Paddock Wood Church, in 1883, the son of a labourer, and later attended Paddock Wood village school. When he left it he joined the farm where he stayed until poor health forced him to retire in 1949. In those years he rose, as it were, to become the High Priest of the English Hop Garden, described by Richard Church in 'Whitbread Craftsmen' (Whitbread Library 1948). His daughter, Felicity recalls that Mr. White taught her father all he knew. The gentleman's son with the public school education and the labourer's son with the village school education found harmony in the hop garden.

Whitbread were fortunate that Mr. Waghorn continued with the farm for he had intimate knowledge of it and all its business. His abilities had earned him the position of Company Secretary in 1908 when he was only twenty five years old and later in 1919 he was entrusted with the position of liquidator when the company was wound up. Indeed they were more than fortunate because the years ahead were far from easy and it was his skill, judgment and above all, nerve which carried the farm through a critical period. His patience and attention to detail is recorded in his monthly reports sent to the brewery. Unfortunately, the earliest 1920-1928, if written, are lost, but taking up the story in 1929 he shows a farm which has increased its hop acreage from 161 acres in 1920 to 174 acres and the harvest of that year had been a good one, but, he wrote:

'the present state of the hop market suggests that a loss in the farm accounts is inevitable. Now that the Combine of English Hop Growers has ceased to function, English hop growers have once again been thrown on their own resources in regard to the disposal of their hops. At the moment there is something resembling a panic among hop growers,and ruling prices are well below the price of production. The general feeling of uncertainty in the hop industry is so great that the long advocated reduction in the hop acreage is now almost certain to take place, in fact a number of neighbouring growers have already commenced to grub portions of their plant. As far as we are concerned we suggest maintaining our present acreage. It is possible that a combination of a short crop and a low acreage may lead to a reaction in the near future'.[14]

And so in 1930 he continued with his plans for extra pickers to pick an expected heavy crop from their increased acreage. But that year the weather for picking was very unfavourable and it was an exceptionally difficult picking year. The following year, 1931, he reports:

'Taking everything into consideration 1931 has been one of the most difficult years we have ever had to face at Beltring'.

Unfavourable weather conditions meant the threat of disease and he fought a constant battle against Downy Mildew which was aggravated by damp conditions.

But where other growers were ravaged by the disease he, in conjunction with Wye College under Professor Salmon, conducted spraying experiments with Bordeaux Mixture while the idea was in its infancy in this country. He became the first grower to spray on a commercial scale and several years later when the other Golding growers were only just beginning to take precautions against the disease he was well ahead with his programme, reaping the benefits of his experiments by securing a much larger proportion of the crop. At the same period the hops were also attacked by Red Spider, Hop Blight, Hop Aphids and then later *Verticillium* Wilt. All were approached with the same calm scientific expertise.

The depression in the hop industry meant that expenses had to be kept down and so he reported that they were making every effort to reduce the cost of production; they had reduced the number of hands which would effect considerable saving, only essential repairs were being carried out and only essential manures were being purchased.

And so by good husbandry and wisdom he steered the farm through difficult years which might otherwise have been disastrous, and by 1935 papers in the farm records show a thriving, vigorous farm and moreover a farm which was developing a new industry.

It had become Whitbread's policy to encourage visitors to the farm. As early as 1929 Mr. Waghorn reported that owing to the increase in motor traffic they had, during the picking, shown many parties of visitors around the hop gardens and over the oast houses:

'During the last few years the interest in the firm's hop gardens has increased and in addition to those parties arranged for them from the brewery and the Bottling Stores, many private parties have applied to view the gardens. These parties have come not only from London but from neighbouring coast towns such as Folkestone, Hastings and Margate and it may be of interest to note that in one or two cases the charabancs have advertised Whitbread's Hop Farm as their principal objective in their tour of the hop gardens'.

43

In 1935, the number of charabancs visiting the farm during 20 days of hop picking was 575. Weekend visitors including Sunday day trippers, were estimated to be 4,000 each weekend.

By 1936 the oasts were floodlit and thousands of people were visiting the farm during hop picking and:

> 'All appeared to be interested in what they saw and expressed their appreciation of the various arrangements made for their comfort such as guides and sanitary conditions. The new enquiry office at the entrance to Bell Field has been a great help as has the car park which was taken full advantage of and on some days was full to capacity'.

The visitors saw a farm where the hoppers' conditions were ideal. Mr. Waghorn had inherited from his old master a genuine concern for the welfare of his pickers. When a survey of the farm was made in 1935 it was shown that all 3,930 pickers were accommodated in 762 huts. Adults over the age of 14 years accounted for 2080 of the number with 1250 children, and 600 visitors who lived in the huts made up the number. However it was estimated that a more accurate total would be 4,830. There were constant improvements to the living conditions and although pickers were allowed to come on the basis of good character (undesirables were weeded out) allowing Mr. Waghorn to report constantly that picking was carried out in a quiet and orderly manner, he mainly attributed this to the fact that the pickers appreciated the many arrangements which had been made for their comfort and well being.

He also reported in 1935:

> 'We have carried out improvements to the camps which were very much appreciated by the pickers, especially the converted cookhouses and the concrete paths around some of the huts. . .the hot water apparatus newly installed on our Bell Common camp is working well and provides a plentiful supply of hot water to the pickers, a great boon, especially in the mornings. The camp was inspected by Sir Kingsly Wood who expressed his perfect satisfaction with all that he saw and complimented us on the way our pickers were treated and the provisions made for their welfare'.

But for all that has been said about the hoppers – where did they come from? A survey made by the farm in 1939 shows that they were composed of 908 families who came from:

44

South East London . . . . 504 families
East London 224
South West London 27
North West London 6
London EC1 10
West London 25
North London 13
Home Counties 68
Paddock Wood area 31

Some of these areas were to become very significant for other reasons in a very short time.

Preparations
for Picking

THE PREPARATIONS FOR the hoppers and the visitors were immense. All the pickers had to be informed by post when picking would begin, this being known as a bin ticket. This arrangement had been introduced to avoid the old way of wandering down into Kent to find work without making any arrangements for accommodation and work. The railway and the bus company had to be informed, the missions to be advised, the shopkeepers who ran shops on the site contacted, the local publicans alerted, refuse collections arranged, the visitors' refreshment tent erected and the icecream man told – not forgetting the artists' engagements for concerts. All this created an atmosphere of festival for what was often called the Annual Festival in the Kentish hop gardens.

Mr. Waghorn and his staff took the preparations in their customary calm orderly routine and early in the morning of the first working day faced nearly four thousand hoppers assembled on Bell Common for the traditional reading of The Rules. These had been sent by post to all pickers with their bin tickets and were made in the best interest of both the farm and the pickers; some were obviously made through experience!

Rules to Pickers

1. Bin Tickets are supplied on the understanding that holders guarantee sufficient picking strength at the bins. Each bin ticket should represent at least two adults, with family under 14 years

of age, and ticket holders who fail to supply this picking strength will not be granted tickets in the future.

2. Pickers who after receiving tickets find that they are unable to get away, must either return the tickets promptly to us or be responsible for the good behaviour of the persons to whom they give the tickets.

3 Pickers will be notified in good time when to come down for the picking. Persons arriving before such notice is received by them will be refused admission.

4. Bookers have special instructions to collect all tickets before pickers commence work. Persons unable to produce official tickets will be refused.

5. Watchmen are employed for the purpose of attending to pickers' wants as to straw, firing etc. and any complaints must be made to them. Pickers who cannot get reasonable attention should mention the matter at the farm office.

6. Firing is put down at each house or tent each day. Any person taking firing belonging to someone else, or otherwise committing wanton mischief, will be immediately discharged, and paid off at the rate of one penny per basket of hops picked.

7. After the tally has been set, and not dissented from, anyone going on strike, or leaving work during a strike, or leaving picking before it is finished, will be paid off at one penny per basket.

8. Anyone damaging fruit trees will be at once discharged.

9. Pickers are warned to be very careful with all lights as a precaution against fire. It must be clearly understood that all goods brought down by pickers are held by them entirely at their own risk and the Company does not accept any liability for any damage or loss to Hop Pickers' effects while on the farm.

10. Pickers who desire bin tickets, but have not held them before, should write stating the number of the Company in which they worked the previous year.

11. When application is made for tickets it is important that changes of name and address should be clearly notified.

12. Although ample hut accommodation is provided, pickers are requested to assist us in preventing overcrowding by only bringing down their own children.

13. Dogs are not permitted on the farm, and watchmen have instructions to refuse pickers who bring them.

14. Pickers are expected to put all refuse into the dustbins provided, and occupiers of huts will be held responsible for the proper use and conditions of the dustbins allotted to them.

15. No person (adult or child) who at any time prior to the commencement of picking, has been in contact with a person suffering from any infectious or contagious disease will be allowed on the farm. This rule will be strictly enforced, and ticket holders will be responsible for the pickers who accompany them.

Every letter is answered whenever possible by return of post. Any applicant therefore not receiving a reply within the four days should write again, being very careful to give the proper address. As in the past, we desire to make the pickers as comfortable as possible, and their assistance is looked for to aid us in this.

FINALLY, the hops must be picked cleanly, and not in bunches. Any picker disregarding this rule will be discharged, and not allowed to come another year.

After the reading came the great moment when picking actually began. The unknowing might assume that this vast crowd simply wandered off and picked hops. It was rather a highly organised operation.

Up to the end of the nineteenth century the appearance of the hop gardens had changed little over the centuries. Hops were still grown on poles which stood in groups of 2, 3 or 4, at a distance of about 6ft. apart. An acre of ground needed 3,600 poles.

When the hops were ready a hop cutter using a tool called a hop-dog, which had a knife on one side and a hook on the other, cut the bine about the roots and then, hooking up pole and bine and all, laid it across the picker's bin.

'Down comes a hop pole, and away goes a swift hand up it, plucking the flowers into a canvas bin upon a wooden frame, carefully avoiding the leaves till it gets near the top of the pole, when with one stroke it rubs off all that remains, the few little green leaves at the top doing no harm. The pole with the bine stripped of its flowers is then thrown aside just as the cutter who has served eight or nine in the interval drops another pole across the bin'.

This scene was described in Murrays' Handbook of Kent in 1877 but only thirteen years later John Bickerdyke was describing how the poles were being supplemented by wires arranged in various ways, sometimes running from pole to pole and sometimes the wires leaving the poles at right angles were attached to pegs on the ground. Wirework eventually replaced the traditional pole work but the older generation among Mr. Waghorn's pickers would have remembered the old cry of 'Pull no more poles', which came at the end of the day when the oasts were full of hops for drying.

But the organisation did not change. Mr. Waghorn's eager crowd was divided into groups of sixty picking bins called a drift. Each bin was manned by at least four pickers making a workforce of 240 people with a Booker in charge assisted by a Measurer. The drift was then subdivided into ten sets of six bins each supervised by a bin man who had to assist both his Measurer and his pickers and was responsible for seeing that the ground occupied by his set was cleared of hops before moving on.

The direction was tightly supervised. At Beltring most of the gardens were double planted and each 242 hills (plants) were marked with a set stump as a guide post and the pickers worked eleven hills to the stump and eleven away and no one ever strayed from the pattern.

The Measurer for the whole drift was responsible for seeing that the drift worked and moved together. He also weighed the hops when stripped from the bines. They were put into large sacks called pokes and held by the binman who kept count of the ten bushel sacks as they were tipped in. The Booker recorded the tally for each picker and in the evening transferred his records into his day book. The picker was given his own record in the form of a token or a tally stick.

Each drift had a poke wagon allotted to it and the driver only loaded pokes from his own drift so that the oast houses could be loaded with the same kind of hops from the same garden.

At the end of a long day's work the hoppers returned to their huts and their cooking. The rest of the day was their own!

The Farm
Worker

HERE WAS A GROUP OF people who were of even greater importance than the pickers who dominated the farm for only a few weeks of the year. This group was the farm workers who day after day, week after week, month after month, and year after year, worked the cycle of husbandry, in all weathers. Their wives joined them for the seasonal work on the farm. They mostly lived in farm cottages and 'lived' the farm. As Mr. Arthur Brooks commented at the age of 77 years, 'I don't have to remember it, I live it'.

Whitbread was concerned about the welfare of their workers, making constant improvements to their housing. Felicity Waghorn recalls baths and plumbing in the 1930s when this was quite 'something' – and they were encouraged to look after their gardens and allowed a day off on a rota basis for gardening, and in the days before the National Health Service, encouraged to belong to the District Nursing Association for which Mrs. Waghorn collected from them 1/7½d a quarter. Social life was not forgotten with the mammoth task of organising the annual dinner for the workers and their families.

Here as a tribute to the hop workers of Kent is a list of 54 farmworkers in 1938 on one large farm, their work descriptions and the wages they were paid. The Agricultural Wages Board had in 1937 raised the minimum wages of the general farm worker labourer from 33/- to 34/- a week. Many of them joined the farm as young men and stayed to receive long service awards from Whitbread who regarded them as loyal and faithful workers. It is a good representaive list because nine of them were born in the 19th century and joined the farm with Mr. White.

PARTICULARS OF STAFF

Name & Address	Work	Wages per week
ACOTT, Dyson (Lad) H⌐mlet Cottages, B⌐ ring, Paddock Wood	Office	25/-
ACOTT, Fred North Cottage, Snoll Hatch, East Peckham	General Labourer Manure Sower Hop Earther Hop Measurer	34/- & piece worker
ACOTT, George Hamlet Cottages, Beltring, Paddock Wood	Head Horseman	44/-
BANFIELD, Robert (Old age pensioner) (Address as under)	Horseman	24/-
BANFIELD, Cecil Waggon Lane, Beltring, Paddock Wood	Head Horseman	44/-
BIRD, Richard Mount Pleasant, Paddock Wood	Office Boy	15/-
BISHOP, Albert P.J. Leys Cottages, Beltring, Paddock Wood	General Labourer Wirework Man Oast Hand	34/- & piece worker
BISHOP, Percy W.G. New Inn, Fowl Hall, Paddock Wood	General Labourer Oast Hand	34/- & piece worker
BLOXHAM, Allan R. Glenmead, Maidstone Road, Paddock Wood	Engineer Wash Mixer	45/-
BLOXHAM, Maurice G. 1 Hamlet Cottages, Beltring, Paddock Wood	Tractor Driver General Labourer Oast Hand	34/- & piece worker

BROOKS, Arthur Hamlet Cottages, Beltring, Paddock Wood	Farm Carpenter Party Guide	53/-
BROOKS, Charles Hamlet Cottages, Beltring, Paddock Wood	Bailiff	65/-
BROOKS, Edward Jnr. Grape Vine Cottages, Beltring, Paddock Wood	Tractor Driver General Labourer Wirework Man Oast Hand	34/- & piece worker
BURGESS, Alfred J. Cats Place, Church Road, Paddock Wood	General Labourer Hop Measurer	34/- & piece worker
BUTCHERS, Arthur Lilly Hoo Cottages, Beltring, Paddock Wood	General Labourer Hop Dresser & Earther Oast Hand	34/- & piece worker
BUTCHERS, Benjamin Leys Cottages, Beltring, Paddock Wood	General Labourer	34/-
BUTCHERS, Jack Little Brookers, Beltring, Paddock Wood	General Labourer Hop Dresser Mower Hop Dryer	34/- & piece worker
BUTCHERS, Reubin B.T. 1 Victoria Villas, Old Kent Road, Paddock Wood	General Labourer Hop Dresser Mower Hop Dryer	34/- & piece worker
CONSTANCE, Henry Mill Field Cottages, East Peckham	General Labourer Wirework Man Hop Dryer	34/- & piece worker
DAVIS, Arthur Bridge Cottages, Five Oak Green, Paddock Wood	General Labourer Manure Sower Hop Digger Oast Hand	34/- & piece worker

ELLIS, Isaac W. Old Merry Boys Cottages, Snoll Hatch, East Peckham	General Labourer Manure Sower Hop Dresser Oast Hand	34/- & piece worker
FAITHFUL, F.A. Pretoria Cottages, Paddock Wood	Hut Repairer Assistant Carpenter Head Camp Overseer	41/-
FLINT, James Lilly Hoo Cottages, Beltring, Paddock Wood	Head Horseman	44/-
GILBERT, Herbert Brook Cottage, Tudeley Road, Five Oak Green, Paddock Wood	General Labourer Manure Sower Hop Dresser Oast Hand	34/- & piece worker
GREEN, Charles 5 Mount Pleasant, Paddock Wood	Horseman	34/-
GRIMES, J.T. Park Cottages, Waggon Lane, Beltring, Paddock Wood	Women's Foreman Cant Hop Gardens Hop Dryer	44/-
HALLAM, Vincent Beltring Cottages, Paddock Wood	General Labourer Hop Earther Oast Hand	34/- & piece worker
HOBBS, Alfred Barrack Row, Yalding	General Labourer Wood Cutter Hop Measurer	34/- & piece worker
JENNER, Charles 6 Sunnyside, Five Oak Green, Paddock Wood	General Labourer Wirework man Oast Hand	34/- & piece worker
KEMP, Albert E. Lydd Cottage, Five Oak Green, Paddock Wood	General Labourer Manure Sower Oast Hand	34/- & piece worker
KING, Arthur Herbert Leys Cottages, Beltring, Paddock Wood	General Labourer Wirework Man Oast Hand	34/- & piece worker

MARTIN, Frank Grape Vine Cottages, Beltring, Paddock Wood	General Labourer Manure Sower Hop Dresser Hop Dryer	34/- & piece worker
NOAKES, Albert Sunnyside, Five Oak Green, Paddock Wood	General Labourer Head Wirework Man Hop Dryer	34/- & piece worker
PADGHAM, Thomas A. Lilly Hoo House, Beltring, Paddock Wood	Gardener Hop Dryer	46/-
POILE, Clifford W. Station Road, Paddock Wood	General Labourer Assistant Carpenter	36/-
RUSSELL, George Lilly Hoo Lodge, Beltring, Paddock Wood	Horseman	34/-
PHIPPS, Albert Easterfields, Golden Green	General Labourer Oast Hand	34/- & piece worker
PHIPPS, Jack (Lad) Sycham Lane, Capel, Paddock Wood	Horseman	16/9
PHIPPS, William G. Sycham Lane, Capel, Paddock Wood	General Labourer Oast Hand	34/- & piece worker
SANDERS, Frank (Lad) Bell Lane Cottages, Beltring, Paddock Wood	Horseman	20/11
TAPP, William Yalding	Horseman Oast Hand	34/-
TAPP, Reginald J. New Barnes, Lucks Lane, Paddock Wood	General Labourer Horseman	34/-
TAYLOR, Percy H. Beltring Cottages, Paddock Wood	Garden, Engine & Car Park Marker	46/-

UNDERDOWN, Charles Beltring Corner, Paddock Wood	Tractor Driver General Labourer Oast Hand	34/- & piece worker
VANNS, Tom Maidstone Road, Paddock Wood	Horseman Oast Hand	34/
WELLS, Fred James (Lad) The Bungalow, Laddingford, Yalding	General Labourer Assistant Carpenter	29/3
WELLS, George Skinners Cottages, Beltring, Paddock Wood	General Labourer Shepherd	36/- & piece worker
WHITHAM, Victor Old Merry Boys Cottages, Snoll Hatch, East Peckham	Tractor Driver General Labourer Oast Hand	34/- & piece worker
WICKHAM, Frederick Mill Field Cottages, East Peckham.	General Labourer	34/- & piece worker
WINCH, George West Pikefish, Laddingford, Yalding	General Labourer Tractor Driver	34/-

The following man is employed during the summer and Hop picking only

WEST, Sydney Chequers Inn, Tudeley, Tonbridge	Painter Assistant Carpenter Hop Measurer	36/6

Their farmworkers' numerous tasks in the farming year are best described by Mr. Waghorn for the year October 1937 - October 1938.

'**October**. The work this month has mainly consisted of clearing up after the hop picking. Oast houses and pickers' huts have been well cleaned out and all rubbish destroyed. A good start has been made with all the usual autumn work. Delivery of manure and shoddy, has begun and owing to the picking finishing early and the mild fine weather it has been possible to begin the ploughing much sooner than in most years. It will be necessary to plough in an increased quantity of stable manure and shoddy per acre this season as no doubt much of the manurial value obtained from this source was washed out of the soil by the excessive flooding during the whole of last winter and spring.

This mild winter has caused weeds, chiefly chickweed, to grow very freely and unless there is a good sharp frost they may be difficult to cover in neatly with the plough.

We are well forward with the wire work repairs and renewing of poles where necessary. The bedded sets have been dug up in readiness for replanting dead hills where required.

Good progress has been made with the cutting of the bines. A quantity of these are to be saved to provide pickers' beds for 1938, the remainder will be burnt as a preventative measure against the spread of disease.

All the tractors and the spraying machines are being dismantled and thoroughly overhauled and where necessary will be sent away for repairs and renewals. Owing to the conditions under which our Bordeaux Spraying Machines work and the nature of the mixture used, the general wear and tear on certain parts is extremely heavy and this thorough annual overhaul is decidedly necessary.

A much needed hard road has been continued over certain fields. The brushing out of certain ditches has begun and the flood ditch which was badly overgrown with bushes is now being cleared of brushwood and well dug out to carry away flood water.

November. The weather during the month has been exceptionally suitable and all work on the farm is more forward than it has been for many years at this time. This applies especially to the ploughing, which if weather permits, will be finished early in December – nearly a month sooner than usual.

Other seasons work that is well forward is the cleaning out of ditches and trimming back of poplar lewing.

The task of overhauling the wirework is being continued and new poles, wires, hooks, stumps are being fitted where necessary.

In addition to these ordinary repairs we have entirely renewed the small wires and rehooked Ten Acres and Tank and Roughsand and are well on with Orchard Garden.

There is very little to show for this work but it involves a great deal of labour. By carrying out this maintenance thoroughly each year our wirework is kept in really first class condition.

According to custom all gardens have been inspected for dead hills and new bedded sets planted where required.

Work has begun on cutting the underwood in America Shaw. A good deal of brushwood for the pickers and also cordwood for charcoal will be obtained from this source.

Delivery has been taken of two new Cletrac crawler tractors. There are now six working tractors.

December. Following the annual examination of the heaters and pipes at the Bell Oasts the necessary repairs are now finished and they should remain in good working order for some years. There are still repairs to be carried out in the other oasts. The main work other than this has consisted of poplar trimming, repairing and renewing wirework, repairing gates, roads, carting brush and cordwood.

The women had repaired all the pokes and bincloths.

The work of building the new cart shed and concrete yard at the back of the farm is being proceeded with and when finished will prove not only very useful but greatly improve the appearance of the buildings at this particular spot.

Many yards of first class fencing have been erected during the autumn of 1936 and 1937.

January 1938. The weather throughout the month has on the whole been very favourable and so progress has been made with all outside work. Hop ploughing was finished last month and a good start has been made with ploughing back. Delivery of lump lime is now nearly finished and is being carted and spread on the gardens due to be treated this season (one ton per acre to a third of the acreage every year).

All gardens have received Sulphate of Potash. This fertiliser is not applied to induce quantity but to encourage the development of the foliage and accentuate maturity at the proper time. The gardens have also had a dressing of Steamed Bone Flour required to stimulate root development.

The rest of the work consists of trimming hedges, and the usual winter round, carting brushwood, trimming poplars, digging outside of gardens. The new cart shed behind the farm office is finished and work on the new tractor shed is being proceeded with.

February. Ploughing back of the hops is being continued.

Towards the end of the month the hop digging was begun. (Digging the unploughed slips on each side of the hills). This operation is preparatory to the main cultivation and is in readiness for the hop dressing which begins on the first of March.

The stringing of the hops started on the 16th. This is being done by the usual gang of women.

Two men have been burning the cordwood for charcoal. There are about 100 cords of this to burn which has been cut up on the farm, and it should not be necessary to purchase any charcoal for the next year or so.

The work of cutting out the underwood continues, the new tractor and implement shed has been built, two men are still occupied in the annual cleaning out of the hot air furnace pipes in the Bell Oasts.

March. The dressing of the hops (cutting back the first growth to the crown of the hill) was begun as usual on March 1st. Ploughing back and digging the hops between the hills is now finished and a good start has been made with the first spring cultivations using both tractors and horses.

The stringing work is very well forward, the general farm work is well forward, two men have finished the annual examination of the Bell Oasts and in addition to these jobs which have taken up a large proportion of labour, the following has also been done during the month: general repairs, painting buildings, fencing, sowing manure, cutting brushwood, burning charcoal, making up a new short road round the farm building, pegging hops etc.

April. Dressing and stringing were finished by the middle of the month, and since then the cultivators have been continually at work using both tractor and horses and the entire acreage has been cultivated four times.

The painting of shafting, fans, and chimneys at the Bell Oasts is being done. The work of cutting down old oak and fir trees has begun. These are all dead in the tips and not growing. A start has been made on repairing the old straw barn at Lilly Hoo. A new pneumatic tyred trolley has been built and our carpenter has made a really good job of it.

In addition to the above mentioned jobs, the following have also been done during the month: general repairs, making up of roads, finishing new road and curbing around the new implement shed, fencing, carting brushwood, painting cottages, etc.

May. The women began tying hops on the 4th May (that is training up selected bines and pulling out surplus growth). This work termed 'firsting' was finished by the end of the month. They are now on the 'seconding' – that is continuing the training.

Cultivation with both horses and tractors has been continued. Weeds have not been very troublesome but there is some chickweed showing among the hills and 'chopping' (moving the soil around the hills with plate hoes) has begun.

June. All gardens have had their last dressings of manure. Earthing began towards the end of the month, and this year we are only covering each hill with two shovelsful of earth instead of four. This is done in order not to check the growth any more than can be helped. Cultivation has continued and all gardens are free from weeds. Other work that has been proceeded with is as follows: repairs to oast roofs, repairs to cottages, making new carts, erecting hop screening, moving roadsides, trimming car park lawns and roads.

July. Hoeing out the weeds and general cultivation is being continued. During the month repairs and renewals have begun in both the hop pickers' camps. The roads surrounding the Beltring Farm buildings have been tarred and rolled, also the road surrounding the oasts at Bell Field have been resurfaced, tarred, gritted and rolled and this greatly improved the appearance of this part of the farm which during picking time is greatly used by visitors. The remainder of the work this month has consisted of: placing screening around the hops in exposed places, mowing outsides of gardens and camps, earthing hops, repairing oasts etc.

August. The work this month has consisted mainly of repairing and painting huts; concreting cook houses; brushing back poplars round outsides of gardens; cleaning and whitewashing of oasthouses; carting straw for the pickers' beds; painting some of the gates; carting hop bins; putting in bin cloths and general preparations for hop picking.

September. The hop picking began here on Monday September 5th and finished on September 22nd having occupied 16 working days. It was one of the shortest pickings for some years.

The average number of bins employed was 877 and the total number of pockets packed was 2,258 – the total hundredweight will be in the region of 3,400. The tally was fixed to begin at five baskets to a shilling. It was reduced for the last four days to four baskets to a shilling. It was found necessary to do this because some of the hops in the later gardens being on the small side and the pickers' earnings per day were not up to the average of 7/- per bin.

October. The main work this month has been of a seasonable character – clearing up after hop picking and preparing the gardens for the new season's work. The pickers' huts have been cleaned out and refuse destroyed; all hop bins have been repaired and stored away; bin-cloths and pokes washed and a start made with the annual usual autumn and winter works such as cutting off and burning old bines and tying up sufficient of these for hop pickers' bedding for 1939'.

This then was the picture of a farm in Kent. . . hops and hoppers and huts and workers and work. . .all were to be severely tested as together they faced the most unusual period in the history of the farm.

The Farm at War

URING THE SECOND World War Beltring Farm in common with every other element of wartime Britain had its own particular private war to fight in coping with the immense problems which war time conditions presented.

They had been used to coping with regiments of hoppers but soon after the 1939 harvest they were called upon to house the first Battalion of the Queen Victoria Rifles. The Bell Oasts were requisitioned by the War Office on the understanding that they would be vacated in time for Mr. Waghorn to prepare for the next harvest. In the event there was no competition for accommodation. The men arrived on November 1st and left on May 10th, 1940 for a mobilisation centre at Ashford where they were ordered to France on the 21st and landed there on the 22nd and took part in the defence of Calais. When this fell to the Germans on May 26th only 120 men managed to return to England. Those who were not killed were captured and spent vital youthful years in captivity, not returning until 1945.

During the time they were at the farm such good relationships were made that the men often returned for reunions and in September 1984 a permanent memorial was opened at the farm in the form of an exhibition commemorating the time that the Q.V.R. spent there. A letter at the farm records the thanks of Major General Dalby on behalf of his regiment for all the kindness and consideration received by them from Mr. Waghorn.

Another 'military' operation was the arrival of the Land Army whose presence is also commemorated at the farm in the form of a lady's figure dressed in Land Army uniform.

The major problem of the 1940 wartime harvest was that evacuation, work on munitions and the demands of the armed services meant that many of their traditional pickers were unavailable and Whitbread's found that they had a workforce of only 2000 instead of their normal 4000. They were of course not the only farm affected in this way and a call went out from the Kent War Agricultural Executive Committee for local people to help with the bumper harvest. Appeals were made to consider it as a form of emergency. Driven from their homes by the German raiders hundreds flocked to the accommodation offered in the hopper huts and set to work to gather in the hops as their response to the terrors they had experienced in London. 'We cannot, we will not be broken', one lady was quoted as saying.

They came to a countryside prepared for them because the only conditions under which the government allowed picking to go on was that suitable air-raid precautions should be taken. The farm had been instructed to be prepared to cope with lighting restrictions in the huts by fixing doors and windows with black-out materials, while the cookhouses were provided with a screen to stand in front of fires to prevent the glare being visible from above. Twenty two of the farm workers were trained as Air Raid Precaution Wardens and the strangest list of equipment ever to appear on the farm is preserved:

22 suits of anti-gas clothing (jackets, trousers, gloves, hoods, rubber gum boots).
22 sets of underclothing.
22 boiler suits.
22 tin hats.
17 Civilian Duty Respirators.
5 General Service Respirators.
2 stretchers.
1 large A.R.P. First Aid Box.
50 Triangular bandages.
4 sets of splints.
2 dozen fire extinguishers, ½ doz. refills.
2 man manual pump with 2 × 60 ft. hose with necessary couplings.
22 eye shields.

Casualty stations were built where slight casualties could be treated whilst more serious injuries would be treated in a temporary hospital inside the farm buildings. The farm wardens were joined by sadly experienced A.R.P. workers among the pickers who offered their services to the farm.

A quarter of a mile of trenches were dug in preparation for the expected 4000 pickers, lest they should be attacked from the air while in the fields. This took two months. The oasts and buildings were equally well protected, twelve fire hydrants and 1500 ft. of hose could be brought into play in the event of incendiary bombs. Some of the buildings were camouflaged and the white cowls were painted black.

But in spite of the organisation the first raid of the season one Sunday dinner time, took everyone by surprise. A nurse with the church army describes how everyone was in the public houses and how she was kept busy for hours afterwards dealing with casualties who were knocked over in the stampede caused by the sound of the siren. Later she took part in explaining to the hoppers what to do next time they heard the siren. They did not have to wait long and the pickers had many hair-raising experiences as the Battle of Britain was fought overhead with machine guns blazing in the sky, high-explosives falling and the race to the trenches for cover. One visitor to the farm on business found that his business was somewhat curtailed by the fact that an aeroplane had crashed in the middle of a hop garden which required Mr. Waghorn's attention. No one had been injured.

Felicity Waghorn has vivid memories of the Battle at Beltring. So many bombs dropped on the farm that it was considered that the planes observed the hopper huts and thought they were military buildings. A retired worker, Mr. Banfield, was employed full time to fill in the bomb holes using a cart filled with dirt and the government allowed the farm 9/- a hole towards the cost.

During the night of September 11, the huts were bombed whilst the pickers slept, causing slight injuries. It was fortunate that the worst raid occurred after the majority of the families had returned home to London, but there were still 80 families who had been given permission to remain until they could be officially evacuated. On October 5, five high explosive bombs fell on the farm, the worst damage being caused in the centre of the camp where one bomb wrecked thirty huts causing six deaths and twelve casualties. The Red Cross were immediately on the scene taking over responsibility for the welfare of the bereaved and casualties. The pickers had lost their all and were fed and clothed by the Red Cross, the wounded were visited in hospital and a detailed report sent to the farm. This reveals that all of them had been bombed out of their homes in London, out of the shelters where they had taken refuge and now they had been bombed out again.

In spite of the hazards of that year the pickers arrived in strength for the 1941 season, still under wartime conditions, with gas masks, identity cards, ration cards, blackouts in the camps, but a clear, free sky overhead and un-needed trenches. They were not to know that two years later a new danger from the London sky would send them to Beltring three weeks before hopping began in order to escape from the flying bombs dropping on their homes.

Throughout the war years, the pickers were united by an even stronger bond than traditional hop picking, and when victory over Japan was announced on September 2, 1945, signalling the close of hostilities, what place could have been better to celebrate than in the hop fields at the beginning of another hopping. After all, as they had said on many occasions, that's why they were picking hops, to make sure there was enough beer for the victory celebrations.

A large celebration party was held for the children on September 16th.

The war years at least shielded the farm from a pending problem. During 1937 Mr. Waghorn had received a visit from Mr. Hinds of Messrs. McConnel and Hinds, the inventors of the English hop picking machine. He came to give particulars on the working of the machines and the experiments they had carried out during the last hop picking and said that the cost of labour was half that of hand picking. Consequently Mr. Waghorn went in September to see a demonstration of the machine at Messrs. Whitehead and Coleman at Smugley Farm, Goudhurst. The inventors claimed that it was not their intention to oust the pickers but to meet the situation should there be a shortage of pickers. Whilst Mr. Waghorn could see that the machine had advantages in that it could work during wet weather and could work for twenty four hours a day, and that it appeared to be mechanically satisfactory, he was not having any difficulty in finding pickers. He knew that if these machines ever came into full use they would prevent thousands of poor people from having their working holiday. He also realised that the machines would have an effect on the local public houses who relied on their annual 'harvest' serving the thousands of pickers. For these reasons he decided not to take any action about machines for the time being. Indeed he never did take any action and remained loyal to his pickers and the traditonal ways and did not mention the machines again in any of his reports.

For health reasons Mr. Waghorn retired in 1949. Sir Sidney Neville, the Chairman of Whitbread in a farewell speech said that not only was he the greatest authority on hops he was also a specialist in the welfare of his pickers. In the same speech he said that picking machines would not be used yet because hand-picking was more efficient and because it provided a pleasant holiday for thousands of pickers. Yet by 1953, only four years later, letters began to arrive at the farm from families who claimed to have picked for generations and who expressed shock and bewilderment because they had been informed that they would no longer be required for picking because hop picking machines had been introduced. Taking the onslaught of these charges was Major Barsley who had succeeded Mr. Waghorn as farm manager.

Obviously from then onwards the machines could not be ignored but Whitbread maintained their loyalty to a reduced number of traditional pickers for as long as possible and eventually they were almost the last in the district to use hand-pickers.

However all this took place in a certain atmosphere. Pickers had themselves begun to change and this was observed in the Kent and Sussex Courier in 1949. They seemed to be of a different class. In the past they had come by the hopper special trains but now they were beginning to arrive in their own transport and, moreover, bringing caravans for accommodation instead of using the huts. Although picking had always been regarded as a holiday the feeling now was even more pronounced as many of the pickers did not appear to need the money. It had become a holiday with pocket money. At Whitbread a spokesman was reported to have said that their camp was up to holiday standards.

Even though they had hot and cold showers and baths provided in all three camps together with welfare arrangements to cope with every eventuality, pickers were not now dependent on hopping for their holiday. The post-war Welfare State with children's allowances, the post-war rebuilding of bombed slum areas of London, culminated in the late 1950s with the 'You've never had it so good' era and the development of new affordable holiday industries made a hop picking holiday less attractive. Inevitably, as perhaps the inventors of the machine had foreseen, the pickers became difficult to get.

In one short decade, a revolution took place. In 1962 plans were made to convert Bell 1 Oast into a hostel for 40 student pickers. This contained a recreation and dining room, toilet accommodation, and living accommodation for managing staff. Later there were T.V., radio, table-tennis, football and various indoor games to attract the students to a Kentish farm for the hop picking. The cries of 'Oh my darling' filling the air were replaced by voices from Egypt – Yugoslavia – Belgium – Italy – Spain – Germany. All these students were asked to 'bring photographs of your country'.

It was a time of many sadnesses and farewells but not only among the pickers. During the 1950s the Franciscan Mission to Hop Pickers had been aware that conditions were changing and that the number of pickers was falling. In the early days of their mission they had estimated that eight to ten thousand Roman Catholics were unable to attend Mass on Sundays because they were too far from a Catholic Church and it had been their custom to celebrate Mass in the open air taking an altar out into the hop gardens. In 1909 they had reported that 450 hoppers attended mass at Beltring.

Their first action every year was to tour the gardens to bless the crops. They set up a mission tent which was open in the evenings for pickers to write letters and read newspapers. There were lantern lectures for the children and a nursing department with two surgeries a day. As well as this they worked at a bin to maintain themselves. In later years when Brookers Oast went out of use they were able to use that for their living accommodation, chapel and hospital.

Their mission had spread to other villages in the Weald and every year Dr. Peter Amigo, Archbishop of Southwark, who had initiated the mission, made a pilgrimage through the hop gardens. He died in 1949 at the age of 85, a few days after making his 44th visit. The warmth of his obituary in the Kent Messenger speaks for itself. It says that he was known as 'the Bishop of the Kent Hop Gardens' and as a 'Labourer in Robes' and was said to recognise his people over the years through their family likenesses.

But in 1962 the Friars wrote to the farm to say that with fewer hoppers they thought that their spiritual endeavours could be put to better use other than at the hop farm. That year they reduced their numbers to two Fathers and ten assistants. A farm memo comments:

'It looks as though we shall be saying goodbye to them, we shall be sorry to see them go'.

as indeed they did, not returning for the 1963 season.

The Friars' departure also meant the loss of another very familiar figure, Sister Theresa of the Catholic Nursing Institute, who had nursed the pickers' ailments for many years. She wrote a farewell letter to the farm. Also saying goodbye were the Salvation Army, the Church of England Mission, the British Red Cross Surgery and an Oxford University Mission.

And so by 1967 in an entirely different atmosphere three Bruff machines on Beltring and three at Stilstead picked 70% of the 260 acres. The remainder were picked by 120 families of hand-pickers on each farm. The end came as an act of God on the early morning of Sunday, September 15th, 1968 when the River Medway burst its banks after very heavy rainfall and caused unprecedented flooding not only in the Medway valley, but in particular at East Peckham and the hopper camps. Lying as one did at Stilstead, near the river, inevitably the pickers there sustained the initial shock. They had actually been paid off on the Saturday and were preparing to move off when the disaster occurred.

There are many letters at the farm from people who were caught unawares and terrified as the water came rushing into Stilstead camp. Some wrote afterwards describing what happened:

> 'On Sunday September 15th, we were waiting for our motor to arrive to take us home to London when without warning the water just poured in on us and we had to run and leave eveything, all we had was what we had on, my children had not been out of bed long and they were not dressed properly, we just grabbed their coats and we ran. Then we were stranded in the water for about three hours before we could be moved to somewhere dry. First we went on tractors to the oast house, then from there to the mission hall at Golden Green where after all those hours we had our first cup of tea. From there we were moved in army lorries to the T.A. Drill Hall in Tonbridge.'

In fact 230 people were taken to the Drill Hall which during the following night itself became flooded. The pickers were rescued again, this time by an amphibious boat which took them to a temporary rest centre set up at Hugh Christie School where they were fed and looked after by the Women's Royal Voluntary Service.

The 380 pickers at the Beltring camp were evacuated to a centre at Paddock Wood Secondary School where with the help of the W.R.V.S. they were provided with hot drinks and meals the following day. Unfortunately many of the pickers belongings were either completely lost in the flood or completely ruined by it and their letters to the farm afterwards showed that they felt very hard done by. The company itself had great losses of crops and damage to property and thirty employees' houses were flooded to depths of three to four feet but Mr. Pelly, the farm manager, was thankful that with the help of the army, the local authorities, the W.R.V.S. and neighbours there was no loss of life.

The event did, however, lead to the loss of a way of life.

Because of the flood Whitbread felt that they could no longer accept responsibility for pickers in camps and this coupled with the extensive damage to the huts forced them to send a circular letter to all the remaining pickers.

In reply came indignant and shocked letters:

> 'We were very shocked and distressed to receive your letter regarding our not being required for picking this year. . . I have been picking for Whitbread now for 25 years.'

At least one hopper was completely bewildered by the circular and wrote back asking what it meant.

The reply, closing four centuries of Kentish custom, stated starkly:-

> 'It simply means there will be no more hop picking on Beltring or Stilstead farms.'

The mechanical pickers had won.

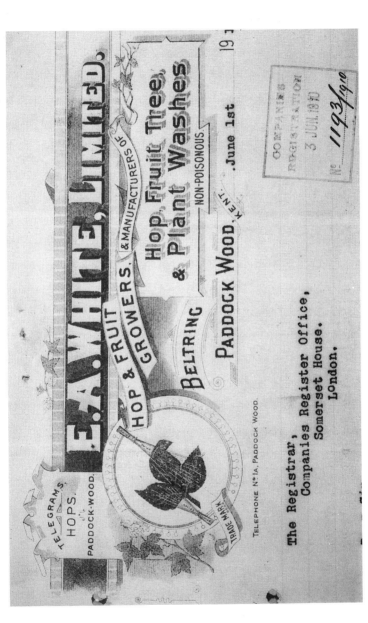

E.A. White's letter heading. Note the telephone number.

Mr. J.H. Waghorn. 'The High
Priest of the English
Hop Garden'.
Whitbread Craftsmen

The flooding of the Medway Valley in September 1968.   *Whitbread*

Part of the pickers' camp, 1936. There were constant improvements and conditions were said to be ideal. West Kent Archives

By 1936 thousands of tourists were viewing Whitbread's hop gardens. West Kent Archives

Verticillium Wilt on Hops

THE FACTS

1. The disease was first discovered at Penshurst, Kent, in 1924 and **is caused by the fungus Verticillium** which is known to live in the soil.

2. **Hills are infected from the soil** through the roots, **not through the air.**

3. Hills with wilt **may** be completely killed but **commonly make complete recovery.**

> e.g. **No bines have wilted** this (1937) season in the original affected garden at Penshurst.

4. The majority, most probably all, the hills in an affected garden are infected with the fungus whether the bines have wilted or not; therefore the disease **does not " spread "** in the usual sense. **Apparent spread** is due to the weather and soil becoming more favourable to the disease.

5. Wilting is primarily caused by soils and weather inducing water logging of infected roots during the summer months before picking.

> The conditions are :—
>
> **SOIL.**
>
> (a)   Local shallow " panning."
>
> (b)   Springs near the soil surface.
>
> **WEATHER.**
>
> (a)   Abnormally wet winter **deficient in frost-action.**
>
> (b)   Wet summer weather, particularly in June and July.
>
> N.B.   Tendency to Wilt becomes greater as the hill becomes older and the roots deeper.

6. **Disease Control.**

> (a)   **New-plantings:**   Avoid soils with high summer water tables.
>
> (b)   **Established Plantations:**   Improve drainage (if possible) to facilitate quick drainage in wet summers and after wet-warm winters.
>
> (c)   It is not necessary to grub wilting hills unless completely dead.
>
> (d)   **Resistant Varieties:**   No varieties have shown outstanding resistance to date.

(Signed)   R. V. HARRIS,

7th September, 1937.   *East Malling Research Station.*

The farmers fought a constant battle against hop diseases.

A group of 'home pickers' at Whitbreads. S. Wood

After listening to The Rules the pickers set to work. West Kent Archives

Malling Rural District Council.

F. MISKIN,

SOLICITOR,

CLERK.

PHONE—WEST MALLING 130/131

Council Offices,

West Malling, Kent.

20th June, 1939.

Dear Sir,

A.R.P. - Lighting Restrictions

As no doubt you are aware it will be the duty of the Police, in time of Emergency, to enforce the lighting restrictions then to be in operation.

I am directed to communicate with farmers in this district, who have huts for the accommodation of fruit and hop-pickers, with a view to steps being taken now so that in the event of an Emergency arising while the huts are occupied, the restrictions as to lighting may be complied with immediately.

For this purpose it is suggested :-

1. That canvas (thick enough to prevent the passage of light and long and wide enough to amply cover the aperture) be affixed to windows and, if necessary, to doors of huts in such a manner that it could be left rolled up in daytime and released when required.

2. An apron, or hood, be affixed to the roof, and a screen be made to stand in front of cook-houses to prevent the glare of the fire being visible from above.

3. A Warden be appointed for each camp to see that all exposed fires are extinguished and generally make sure on your behalf that the regulations are observed.

I shall be glad to know that you will take measures to prepare for any emergency and if Mr. S.L. Bundy, the Council's Inspector, can be of any assistance to you with suggestions or otherwise, please communicate with him at this office.

Yours faithfully,

Miskin.

Clerk.

One of the many problems with which farmers had to cope.   Whitbread Papers

Children in trench watching the Battle of Britain overhead. Whitbread

An abandoned hop garden. A sad sight in the Kentish Weald.

Derelict hopper huts at Barming.

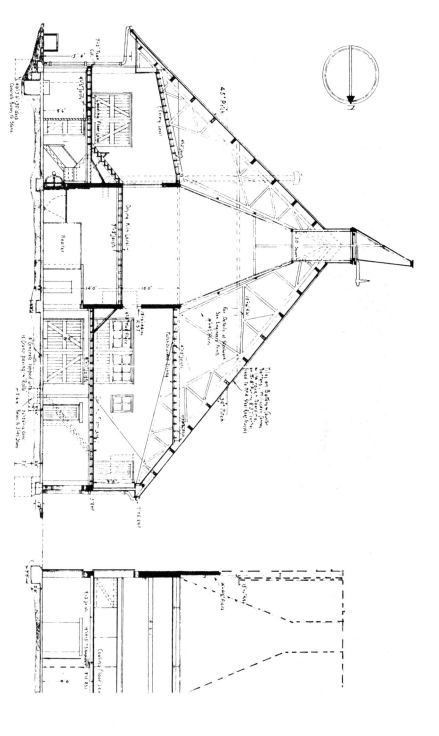

Bell 5. Whitbread Hop Farm. An example of how the development of oasts turned full circle. The kiln and stowage are built under one roof as in the earliest designs.

West Kent Archives

Interior of oast house showing dried hops waiting to be pressed.

Pockets of dried hops. The suspended pocket is receiving the hops from the press on the drying floor above.

The brewery drays in Russels yard. The stabling and maintenance of the horses was an essential feature of a brewery building.

An example of the giant breweries which have disappeared from Kent.

RUSSELL'S GRAVESEND BREWERY, LIMITED.
The Brewery – A View from the River Thames.

FREDERICK LENEY AND SONS,

Phœnix Brewery,

WATERINGBURY.

———o———

Superior
    India Pale,
        Bitter,
           and other Ales.
    Stout and Porter.

———o———

Stores:

    TUNBRIDGE WELLS
        AND
    CHATHAM.

——o——

PRICE LISTS ON APPLICATION.

HOLMES & STYLE,

MEDWAY BREWERY,

MAIDSTONE.

TRADE ✡ MARK

INDIA PALE AND FAMILY ALES.

LIST OF PRICES.

	BARL. 3½ Gal.	KIL. 18 Gal.	FIRKIN 9 Gal.
B B	36/-	18/-	9/-
P A	42/-	21/-	10/6
I P A	50/-	25/-	12/6
X	36/-	18/-	9/-
X X	54/-	27/-	13/6
X X X	63/-	31/6	16/-
Porter	36/-	18/-	9/-
Stout	50/-	25/-	12/6

LONDON STORES :—

BRIXTON ROAD
AND
BLACKHEATH HILL, } Adjoining L.C.& D. Railway Station.

Brewery advertisements from 1875 directory.

The Medieval Brewer past and present. Philip Goacher of Maidstone shows that little has changed in the manufacture of Real Ale today.

Picture curiosities of Ale and Beer

The Oasts

THE HOPPERS HAVE PASSED into folk lore and while most of their huts have long since been cleared away, some, tantalisingly, still lie derelict about the countryside. Fortunately some have been preserved, as at The Museum of Kent Rural Life at Maidstone, and some on the original farm site as at Reed Court Farm, Chainhurst, near Yalding in Kent where they can be seen near the start of the Farm Trail.

Kent is also left with the oasts, a more prominent enduring monument to the hop industry. With their white cowls they have become typical of the Kentish landscape. They have been converted into housing, workshops, stables, museums, and restaurants. However these familiar buildings were not known to the earliest hop growers.

When the green hops were picked from the garden the moisture had to be removed from them to prevent them rotting. This is best done by a controlled heat, joined with movement of air to carry away the vapourised moisture.

In the early days of English hop growing the hops were dried in three ways; either in the roofs of houses, in the sunshine or in existing malt kilns. These three methods were discussed by Reynolde Scot in his book. He advised that these ways were not good enough because the first two were subject to varied degrees of heat according to the weather and the third was a makeshift use of equipment designed for something else. He advised that purpose built oasts such as he had seen on the continent should be built exclusively for drying hops where the heat could be controlled. At this point the English oast was born.

69

Scot's design was a simple timber-framed barn structure 18 to 20ft. long and 8ft. wide and was divided into three sections all under one roof. The partitioning walls were either brick or timber studs covered with lathe and plaster. The fire was placed in a brick furnace in the middle section, (the plenum chamber) under wooden lathes on which the hops were placed for drying, (the drying floor). The green hops came in through the first section, (the receiving chamber) and when dried passed into the third chamber for cooling, (the cooling floor). An opening in the roof provided an outlet for the reek. This basic design did not change for over two hundred years and although an existing barn could be adapted for use as an oast the internal arrangements were always the same. Scot provided an illustration to make his meaning plain.

Towards the end of the eighteenth century the increased acreage of that period put a strain on this system and existing oasts were adapted to a new design . It was found that by removing the internal square kiln to the outside of the oast the whole barn could be used for receiving and cooling and it became a separate stowage. Moreover, multiple square kilns could be built onto the outside of the stowage. This meant that the kilns now needed their own separate roofs and by shaping the roof pyramid style it could act as a flue to encourage the draught, helped by a cowl.

But it was not until the turn of the nineteenth century that the familiar roundel appeared in the landscape, designed in the belief that hops in the corners of kilns did not receive adequate heat. Gradually the countryside became dotted with the new roundels which internally concealed new experimental designs.

Later in the century there was a change of opinion and when farmers realised that they had been misled about the effectiveness of heating in square-kilns they preferred to build new oasts, as need arose, in square-kiln style. The advantage was that they were cheaper to build than the roundels.

Beltring Farmstead Oasts

BELTRING HOP FARM has become famous as the guardian of the oast tradition. It is not known how long hops have been grown at Beltring but William Lambarde's purchase of Beltring Farm in 1574 with four other Wealden farms coincides with the publication of Reynolde Scot's book and the expansion of the Elizabethan hop industry so it would seem likely that the farm would have already had its hop acreage. Unfortunately, the farm has been so well maintained by the Drapers Company and its tenants that buildings which may have revealed past secrets about hop growing have been replaced by new ones. However two oasts on the original farmstead compete with each other in claiming to be the oldest on the Beltring complex; the Long Oast built by the brothers Thomas and William Cheesman in 1823 and Guests Oast also built by the Cheesmans before 1840.

The Long Oast was a new built oast of brick and weatherboarding and designed to combine the old idea of the square internal kiln with the need for more drying space. Here four internal kilns 17 x 10ft. were built under one roof, two either side of a 4ft. central passage way from which the fires were fed. Above the drying floor the kilns were shaped in the pyramid style and the roof timbers lined with lathe and plaster and gathered into a cowl opening at the roof line. The central passage was repeated on the drying floor area and the green hops were received into it from an outside stairway. When the kilns had been loaded from the passage and the drying process finished the hops were scooped into the passage again and thrown down from the opening at the end of the passage into the ground floor cooling room. The pressing took place underground. A well, or hole, the size of a hop pocket was sunk into the ground floor and the pocket hung and secured. Then the hops were poured in and a man pressed them by treading inside the sack. This was a very unpopular job and was replaced by mechanical pressing. That oast has not been used for drying since 1919.

During 1982/3 the oast was converted into stabling for Whitbread's horses and the whole building renovated, removing the cowl openings in the roof. The new cement floor removed the last evidence of the underground pressing but its shape and form will always be that of an unusual oast. Standing in the stable doorway the central passage from which the fires were fed can still be seen.

Within a short distance stands Guest's Oast. It took its name from Henry Guest who was Mr. White's chief hop dryer. It was built in the new design of two roundels with a separate stowage. It was held in affectionate memory because it was here that Mr. White conducted his famous experiments with hops. It continued in use until 1945 after which it gradually declined until it was unsafe. It was conserved in 1985 when the roundels were converted into more stabling for horses.

Brooker's Oast lay further afield on what is now the main complex. The name is that of the farmer, Samuel Brooker, who lived in a nearby ancient farmhouse in the eighteenth century. This was demolished when the new farmhouse and buildings described as 'all that message lately erected and built with the newly erected oast' were built between 1840 and 1849.[15]

Inside the oast is a rare survival of an old design. When it was built it was a time of experimentation among farmers and here one of the plenum chambers contains a brick tunnel the apex of which rises almost to the drying floor. This is the stoking tunnel from which two fire places let into opposite walls could be stoked. The space between the tunnel and the kiln wall was used for fuel storage. The door at the end of the tunnel was fitted with a louvre for draught control.

Sheila Kay Smith, the Sussex authoress of the 1930s, describes one of her characters in this situation:

> 'He was standing in the little stoking tunnel that cuts across the roundel of the oast, between two charcoal furnaces. He was adjusting his draughts with a primitive wooden shutter and his face in the crimson light was hawklike and intent'.
> *(Susan Spray 1930).*

More recently it has been described and illustrated by Robin Walton (*Oasts in Kent 1985*).

Although this appears to have been a common design it is said by very senior farmers that such tunnels were removed so long ago that they have been forgotten.

When the oast went out of use in 1948 it was used by the Friars but became redundant when their mission was concluded. A farm memo reported that the kiln roofs were in an advanced stage of dilapidation and the whole building was in a very poor condition and was regarded as being of very little use. Thought was given to the idea of demolishing it and clearing the site for other use. Fortunately this was not done and its eventual conversion to the Oast House Pottery and Craft Centre in 1981 secured the conservation of an example of the hop drying industry. It was also influential in the farm being awarded first prize in a conservation scheme sponsored by the Royal Institute of Chartered Surveyors and The Times Newspaper in 1983. The pottery was removed in 1989 but the oast survived yet again when it was planned to join it to the adjoining Brooker's Farmhouse for inclusion in licensed premises and restaurant. The historical interest of the kiln has been recognised and a safe future assured by Whitbread because the stoking tunnel is to be rebuilt on the museum site as a demonstration model of this old method of hop drying.

These then were the oasts, together with three kilns at Lilly Hoo, (now demolished) which E.A. White had for his use when he came to Beltring in about 1886.

The last oast to be built was Bell 5. This five-kilned oast was built in 1936 and is an example of how the development of the oast has turned full circle. Once again the kilns and the stowage were included in a barnlike rectangular building under one roof. It was built of modern materials including an asbestos roof. The steel girders within replaced the great timber beams of its predecessors. It measures 52ft. 6in. x 106ft. After it was taken out of use it was leased in 1973 to Hop Fix, hop processors who adapted the building to the needs of a factory and the kilns were removed. Fortunately a complete picture of the original oast can be seen on the plans which are deposited with The West Kent Archives Office, Maidstone.[16]

Although no longer an oast its former use is represented by its five cowls and it remains a part of the Bell Oast landscape.

But supreme on the site are the earlier Bell Oasts. These oasts take their name from Bell Field on which they stand, opposite The Bell pub, and were built by E.A. White before 1894 in time for his business expansion.

They comprise four separate oasts, each with five separate circular kilns and are known as Bell 1, 2, 3 and 4 and are said to have been built in that order. The stowage of the kilns do not have identical measurements on plan as the chart shows. They do however have identical measurements in elevation; it is 22ft.to the eaves and 40ft. to the gables. The unifying factor is the kilns which are identical both in diameter and in elevation. They measure 26ft. to the eaves of the kiln and 26ft. from the eaves to the cowls. The cowls measure 12ft. in height and 5ft. at the base. The gantries were added in 1936 and 1937 when Mr. Waghorn wrote of his pleasure that they added much to the appearance of the oasts.

The interesting point is that internally the kilns were built with the tunnels as in Brookers' Oast but with four fireplaces to each kiln. The brickwork where the tunnels have been removed can still be seen.

Apart from this they vary in design. Bell 1 and 2 have two floors comprising a stowage and a cooling floor, while Bell 3 and 4 have three floors comprising a stowage, a poke receiving floor and a cooling floor. All contained accommodation for the dryers who lived and slept in the oasts from Monday to Saturday during hop picking. An area was fitted with bunks, a table, and a food cupboard and there were blinds for the windows. This accommodation was regarded as very important and repairs and upgradings frequently appear in farm memos.

Now approaching their centenary the oasts could tell many stories from their past, of their part in the First World War when Bell 2 was used for vegetable storage and Bell 3 for jam fruit storage for the army; of housing troops in the Second World War and how their cowls were painted black against the attraction of enemy aircraft in the Battle of Britain and how in 1962 Bell 1 was converted into student hop picker accommodation and finally, how in 1981 they became the focus of a new recreational venture which Whitbread wished to promote. The cooling floor of Bell 1 was converted into a museum of rural crafts and the stowage converted into a tea room for visitors to the site. Bell 2 was converted into a museum of hop memorabilia with many other aspects of country life while Bell 3 and 4 for the time being continued to dry hops in the traditional way for the instruction of visitors during hop picking. But for all their stories the most interesting to recall is their life as working oasts.

Fuel Supply

THE EARLY POWER FOR fuelling the oasts was wood, but because the smoke tainted the hops it was replaced by smokeless charcoal. This was made by processing cordwood and for centuries it was used in open fireplaces. A new fuel became available in the eighteenth century when smokeless anthracite could be transported in the Weald by the new roads and the new navigation of the Medway between Maidstone and Tonbridge. Later, in the second half of the nineteenth century when hop production was at its highest point, the new railways were able to transport cheap smoky sea coal and manufacturers found a market in developing enclosed heaters which could burn it. The secret was to divert the smoke out of the oast through flue pipes.

A variety of these new heaters were introduced at Beltring. The earliest type known was a Cockle stove and this was installed in one of the kilns in Brookers. Another kiln was installed with a Nokes heater which had a fine pipe carried right through the drying floor. Another kiln was fitted with a Correco heater, a large unit usually housed outside the oast. The remaining two kilns kept their open fires.

Bell 2 had already been converted to enclosed heaters before Mr. Waghorn began his reports to the brewery in 1929. It was in 1929 that he reported that the workers had taken out the tunnels and fireplaces in Bell 3 in readiness for five sets of heaters to be installed by Messrs. Weekes with five sets of fans and pullies at a cost of £765. Bell 1 was installed with a new hot air drying plant in 1934 when the fuel consumption of the new heaters were reported as being the most economical of all the installations on Bell Common. The remaining Bell 4 retained open fireplaces and Mr. Waghorn reported:

> 'Oasts fitted with various systems of heating and good results obtained by all, even from the old fashioned ones with open fires.'

Fuel costs were always under review and a 1936 statement of fuel costs in Bell 1-5 in 25 heaters was;

Coke 225 tons.
Coal   36 tons.
_____
261 tons.

This equals 52 tons per oast at 26 days drying; equals 2 tons of fuel per oast per day or 1 ton each ten hours drying.

There was also a statement of manpower for the same date:

> 'It takes one man 30 minutes in every hour to stoke the fires in an oast. Therefore it takes a man five hours stoking every drying of ten hours, or ten hours a day stoking working twenty four hours a day.'

New ideas for fuelling the oasts were always being considered. Waghorn reported in 1932 that for some time they had been going into the question of employing crude oil burners for hop drying. He said that the previous year Mr. Lewis of High Tilt, Cranbrook had fitted a crude oil burner to the furnace of his Soroco hot air drying plant and that he had visited him to obtain first hand information. Mr. Lewis had told him that his reasons for using oil burners were that he could not be sure of obtaining sufficient heat with coal and frequently lost valuable time on that account but with the oil burner the heat was in excess of what was required. There was also the advantage of a lower price than coal, there was easier control and it was much cleaner. The temperature could be varied in half the time and carriage was cheaper as oil could be delivered to the farm. His cost of coal for a double loading, 35cwt. at 42/-a ton was £3.13s. 6d, while oil for the same quantity was practically half that price at £1.17s. 6d.

Acting on what he had learned Mr. Waghorn sent to Shell Mex for full particulars as to converting one kiln as an experiment or for converting one whole oast but he did not report on the matter and did not mention oil heaters again until 1938 when he went to see an oast at Buston, Yalding which was fitted with oil heaters. Once again there is no record of his thoughts and it must be assumed that he was satisfied with his existing arrangements and it was not until 1949, possibly even after he had retired that Bell 2 was converted to oil burners. By 1967 Bell 3 had been converted but Bell 1 and 4 remained with coal fires.

It was in 1970 that there was a crisis over supplies of coke for the remaining oasts caused by the phasing out of gas coke supplies by the National Coal Board and at that point all open-fire drying stopped.

The earliest power for drawing the heat up through the hops on the drying floor was natural air sucked and controlled by the cowl which was in turn controlled by the wind. This obviously meant that the draught depended on various weather conditions, and that the dryers were not in control. Experiments were made towards replacing the cowl by installing electric fans to control the draught and in 1935 Mr. Waghorn sets out the various ways in which the electrical power was supplied. This was because the Weald of Kent Electricity Supply Company had considered extending its cable from Paddock Wood to East Peckham and had approached property owners along the route as to their potential demand for power. Clearly he thought that the farm was coping quite well without any outside help and his description of the equipment used presents a lively and interesting parade of machinery. He writes:

'We have further been considering the question of power at our Bell oasts, and while our present arrangements are satisfactory up to a point there are improvements which could be made; and if we do not go over to electrical power the adoption of the following suggestions would make us independent of any outside undertaking and standardise the power plant.

The present power and light system:

Bell 1. Fan driven by belts and shafting – powered by 16hp diesel-oil engine hired for 1934 season from Messrs. Drake and Fletcher.

Bell 2. Fans driven by bolts and shaftings – power supply by Aveling and Porter 12hp portable steam engine.

Bell 3. Fans driven by bolts and shaftings – power supply by old oil (paraffin) engine taken from Triton tractor.

Bell 4. Fan driven by electric motor – power supplied by 12 hp Lister petrol engine and dynamo which also generates current for the whole lighting system on Bell Common and seven lights in the camp.'

He suggested that:

'Bell 1. Purchase the engine which had given every satisfaction.

Bell 2. The Aveling and Porter steam engine unsightly and uneconomical – replace it with diesel engine as above.

Bell 3. Oil engine uneconomic – replace as above.

Bell 4. Replace Lister petrol engine with a higher powered dynamo diesel oil engine with larger dynamo capable of supplying sufficient power for the overhead electric fans in Bell 4 and the lights to all existing oasts and the proposed new oast and Brookers Oast – all a cost of £645.1s. 0d.'

There is no record of when the farm finally submitted to connection with an electricity cable.

A day in the life of the Bell Oasts is best told in Mr. Waghorn's own words, written to the brewery in 1938.

'Beginning on Monday morning when all the oasts are empty the large Bell 5 is loaded first. Hops begin to arrive at about ten o'clock and all five kilns are loaded by eleven o'clock. Normally the drying takes about nine hours and these kilns are therefore unloaded about eight o'clock and are at once reloaded with hops picked during the afternoon. This operation of unloading and reloading usually takes about 2½ hours. The first drying is allowed to remain on the floor for cooling until about four or five the following morning, a period of seven or eight hours. They are then packed into pockets, the work occupying about 2½ hours. This leaves the floor clear for the next load which comes off the kiln at about 7.30 am. This procedure is followed in each of the other oasts.

The Head Dryer has complete control of the operation, the decision as to the proper time for unloading and packing is entirely his as he has had years of experience and stays with each load throughout the drying process. Each dryer has his own method of cooling and the success of the drying depends more on the ability of the dryer than on any particular type of oast or system of heating.

One way is to heap the hops in a lump each side of the presses, another is to spread them thinly over the floor, and still another is to keep each kiln load in separate heaps. Any alteration might affect the dryers' judgment.

This judgment during the cooling period is needed because weather conditions have an important effect.

If it is too hot the hops are inclined to dry further on the floor whereas if it is at all wet or damp, moisture will be absorbed causing them to soften in which case packing is begun quicker than the time described. If there is not a moist atmosphere throughout the cooling period and they have not taken up sufficient moisture they will not reach the desired softness. The whole skill lies in the touch of the dryers' hand and it is remarkable that they make so few errors.'

These simple unsophisticated words, quietly written by 'The Master Craftsman' himself as a part of his normal farm duties will further immortalise the Bell Oasts. These cathedral-like buildings are said to be the largest group of oasts in the world and photographs have been taken to all parts of the world by tourists, student hop pickers and professional photographers. Their importance as buildings and their place in the landscape has been recognised by English Heritage who have ensured their preservation by including them in their list of Scheduled Buildings. Meticulous repair after the hurricane damage of 1987 shows how willing Whitbread are to comply in preserving them for the future.

Kent Breweries

S THE LAST DAYS OF the traditional hop picker were being worked it is sad to record that the era of the local brewer was also drawing to a close. The move by the brewers to use their profits to buy freehold estate, begun in the porter brewing days, had continued and expanded in the Victorian period. Brewers appreciated the advantages of brewing more economically and scientifically by combination and although production was greatly increased the number of breweries declined. Partnerships were formed which were expanded into companies and then companies amalgamated. The figures speak for themselves. In 1840 there were almost 50,000 brewers, including inn keeper brewers, in the United Kingdom, but this number shrank to less than half by 1880 and only twenty years later had been reduced to 6,590. This number was halved by the end of the First World War after the high tax on beer had lessened demand, and reduced again during the depression of the 1930s when big brewers took the opportunity to buy up estate. In 1960 there were only 358 breweries operating in the United Kingdom but during the following ten years 147 were closed, a loss of 41 per cent. During those years 150 companies ceased to trade independently and the structure of the brewing industry was fundamentally changed by mergers and takeovers. This resulted in a small number of national brewers becoming known as The Big Six, (Bass, Allied, Watney/Grand Metropolitan, Whitbread, Courage, and Scottish and Newcastle). The incentive for the big brewers was the extra tied houses gained in the takeovers. This increased the effectiveness of their mass national advertising campaigns and increased the outlets for their new products. The commercial success of the big brewers can be judged by the facts; in 1960 they brewed 45 per cent of the beer brewed in the United Kingdom but by 1969 the figure was 75 per cent and by 1972 it had reached 80 per cent and remains at that level in 1990.

The local, small breweries which were gained in the takeovers, were of little importance to the big brewers because they were building giant new breweries close to the motorways for easier nationwide distribution. The majority of local breweries were demolished, losing not only the historic buildings but countless local individual brews.

In Kent the result of these policies over a long period is a melancholy decline. The county has a long history of brewing and from early times this was a staple industry. In the 12th century England was celebrated for its ale and that brewed in Kent was considered to be the best. It is known that there was an early export market by the fact that 50 barrels of ale were exported from Sandwich to Calais in 1395. Indeed in 1455 in order to protect the maltsters of other places from the competition of the Kentish men it was enacted

> 'that no person in the County of Kent who shall commonly brew any ale or beer to sell, shall make nor do to be made any malt in his house or in any other place to his own use, at his costs and expenses above 100 quarters in the year, under penalty of x li, and this penalty to be in force for the space of five years.'

After the expansion of hop growing in the sixteenth century Kent made use of the local raw material and later the expansion of brewing in the porter era saw the birth of some, and the development of many other breweries, which were to become household names. This was particularly noticeable in growing towns like Maidstone and Canterbury and in ports such as Deal, Dover, Margate, Faversham, the Medway group of Strood, Rochester, Gillingham and Chatham, which contained His Majesty's Dockyard, and Gravesend. Beside the trade engendered from commerce there was the opportunity to supply beer to sea-going merchant ships.

However the increase in Kent brewing was not merely due to the new fashion of porter drinking or to rising population. During the eighteenth century the continual fear of French invasion saw a great concentration of men in the county engaged in its defence. This was at Chatham where the contingent of men in the naval base was swollen when a division of the Marines was established there in 1753. The new style, brick-barrack buildings replacing tenting and billeting of troops also had its effect in Chatham when army barracks were built in 1757 and barracks for the marines in 1783. Further barrack building provided accommodation for thousands of men. This situation together with the social visiting to men stationed there created an unquenchable demand for drink and the area became crowded with drinking shops.

In addition to the troops there were the possible 3,000 men employed in the dockyard in time of war.

The defence of the county against invasion continued to be a priority into the middle of the next century as various projects became outmoded and were replaced. As late as 1867 seventy-six new forts had been been built or were under construction. All this military activity was ably supported by the brewers, and Mr. Presnail records, *(The Story of Chatham, 1952)* that 'breweries and malthouses were somewhat plentiful'.

In Freidrick's *'Gazeteer of the Breweries of the British Isles which have been in Operation since 1875'*, there are listed 6,591 breweries, of which 120 were in 55 towns and villages in Kent. Bearing in mind that by that date breweries were in decline there had probably been a higher number.

From his listings, the major centres of brewing were: Canterbury (6 breweries), Dover (7), Gravesend (6), Maidstone (8), Margate (4), Ramsgate (5), Rochester (4), Sandwich (4), and Tunbridge Wells (5).

Operating on a relatively moderate scale with three breweries were Chatham, Dartford, Faversham, Folkestone, Sevenoaks and Tonbridge.

There were thirteen places with two breweries: Ash (Sandwich), Ashford, Broadstairs, Bromley, Deal, Hadlow, Lamberhurst, Lydd, Meopham, Sittingbourne, Wateringbury, Westerham, and Wrotham.

There were twenty-seven places with a single brewery. These were: Aylesford, Beckenham, Bridge, Bexley, Cranbrook, Eastry, Edenbridge, Great Mongeham, Green Street Green, Hawkhurst, Herne Bay, Hythe, Littlebourne, Northfleet, St. Mary's Cray, Southborough, Staple, Stone, Stourmouth, Tenterden, Walmer, West Malling, Wilmington, Wingham, Wye, and Yalding.

It is obvious that in the Victorian period there was a group of old established brewers who were gradually taken over by newer expanding brewers until they in turn were swallowed by the national concerns.

At the Chatham Brewery the Best family were brewing with a business which expanded not only in the Medway area but to Gravesend in the west, and Sittingbourne, Sheerness and Queenborough to the east. After leasing the Chatham Brewery which stood on the corner of Manor Road, Winch and Sons purchased the business outright in 1894. They combined with Style and Company of Maidstone to become Style and Winch in 1899, and went on to absorb the Lion Brewery at Ashford, the Dartford brewery, Style Place Haiiow, the Lydd brewery, the Vallance at Sittingbourne, Troy Town at Rochester, a small brewery at Frindsbury Road, Strood and the Lion at Chatham.

At Maidstone, Style had already taken over the small brewery of Spencer Bow Swinfen at 22 Week Street and became Holmes and Style in 1866 when he merged with Holmes of the Medway Brewery, built in 1825, in Great Peter's Street on the river bank. This brewery, trading as Style and Winch Ltd., developed into the second largest in Kent before it was taken over in 1929 by the national brewers Barclay Perkins who in turn became part of the national brewers group, Courage, Barclay and Simonds. After brewing was discontinued in 1965 the premises were used as a group distribution centre until they were demolished in 1976 and the site has now been redeveloped for a 'Do It Yourself' complex. Courage also took over the Steam Brewery at Dartford and the Bexley Brewery.

Gravesend, on the banks of the Thames was strategically placed for obtaining the materials for brewing by water transport and also for exporting to London and the Kent coastal towns. An existing West Street Brewery was purchased in 1858 by the Russel family who began a policy of buying other small breweries. At Margate they bought the Fort Brewery, owned by Webb and Co.; at Ramsgate the Fleet Brewery; at Dartford the Wilmington Brewery and in Gravesend itself their largest competitor, the East Street Brewery owned by George Wood and Son. Russel's in their turn were bought out in 1932 by the London Brewer Truman, Hanbury, Buxton and Co. Ltd. They had been renowned for their 'Shrimp' brand beers, most likely remembered in their day by sea going men all over the world. Russel's brewery was demolished in 1950. The East Street Brewery although demolished, continues to serve leisure with its site being part of the Riverside Gardens.

There were smaller purchases with Charringtons buying the Wellington Brewery at Gravesend and the Walmer Brewery while Shepherd Neame bought the Waterside Brewery at Maidstone, which was later demolished and the site, at the bottom of St. Faith's Street, used for car parking.

By far the biggest take-over bids have been by Whitbread. The Margate Brewery owned by the Cobb family, who were also Bankers and Shipping Agents remained a family business until the death of the proprietor in 1937 and it was eventually sold to Whitbread's Brewery in 1960. Brewing was discontinued in 1968 and the brewery demolished in 1970. At Ramsgate they took over Tomson and Wotton as well as many others mentioned in this chapter.

Almost the last brewing took place at Wateringbury village, which lies within the landscape described by William Cobbett in 1823:

> 'From Maidstone to Mereworth is about seven miles and these are the finest seven miles that I have ever seen in all England. The Medway is on your left with its meadows about a mile wide. . .there were hop gardens on both sides of the road. Looking across the river you can see hop gardens and orchards two miles deep. There are orchards and woods of ash and chestnut which add to the beauty.'

Yet set in these idyllic seemingly un-industrialised surroundings and within sight and smell of Cobbett's roadway two extensive breweries were built. The reason was that the River Medway between Maidstone and Tonbridge had been made navigable for barge traffic in 1740 and coal and other commodities for brewing could be transported up river from Maidstone and the end product could be exported by the same means. The breweries were helped further by the opening in 1844 of the railway branch from Paddock Wood to Maidstone which took over much of the river traffic.

The village abounds in springs. Who first realised that there was gold in Wateringbury water for brewing is not known but in 1833 John Beale Jude at 22 years of age was paying poor rates for his brewhouse which appears to have been situated on his father William's shop premises. The shop warehouse with its hoist, can still be seen near The Crossroads. At some point John Beale Jude and Co. built the Kent Brewery. The brewery was most economical with all the ingredients being obtained in the cheapest possible way. Jude is later listed in Kelly's Directory 1867 as brewer, maltster, coal merchant, farmer and hop grower.

In 1870 he took into partnership Mr. Ernest Osgood Hanbury (a member of the Hanbury family of the big brewers, Truman, Hanbury and Bucton Ltd.). From that point the business became known as Jude, Hanbury and Co.

After the death of the founder, the business was carried on through his nephew William Jude, son of his older brother, Thomas, 'Grocer and Draper of Hollingbourne'. William went to live with his uncle having the positions first of Brewers' Clerk in 1861, of Brewer's Manager in 1871 and finally of Master Brewer in 1881.[17] William saw the brewery grow from the employment of 18 men to the employment of 32 men and 2 boys, but it was not until after his death in 1919 that the firm expanded with the purchase of the Vine Brewery at Tenterden, the Dane John Brewery at Canterbury, the East Kent Brewery at Sandwill and the Mackeson Brewery at Hythe. As the business had become based in East Kent the firm transferred their brewing to the Dane John at Canterbury and sold the Wateringbury brewery to the Yalding Soap Factory. In 1930 the business was taken over by Whitbread. In 1989 the site was used for housing development where Hanbury Close recalls the old brewery.

Just south of the Kent Brewery lay what was originally known as Warden's Hill Brewery but in the parish Poor Law Assessments it was known as Phoenix brewery by 1838. Probably founded in the late eighteenth century the owner had considerable financial problems which resulted in his forfeiting the property to pay his debts. It was leased by the new owners to Charles Leney in 1838 and later purchased by his brother Alfred Charles in 1861. Alfred and his son are listed in Kelly's Directory 1861, as brewers, maltsters, brick makers, coal merchants and farmers and hop growers. But, one up on Mr. Jude, they were also proprietors of the gas works which had been established in 1856 and which they ran in conjunction with the brewery. They bought the breweries at Cranbrook, Yalding and Milton (Sittingbourne) and had control of some seventy public houses in Kent and a further number in Sussex. Such events did not pass without comment for Sir Charles Igglesden wrote that he was disappointed when he arrived at Yalding:

> 'to find that the local brewery was standing idle since a big firm came along, purchased it and closed it down as rival. I remember Yalding beer, delicious and pungent not so very long ago.'
> *(Saunters through Kent with Pen and Ink, 1901).*

The firm was taken over by Whitbread in 1927, who continued to trade as Leneys until 1961 when the licensed outlets were sold to Fremlins of Maidstone. Whitbread continued to brew at Wateringbury with Fremlins joining their organisation in 1967 and the brewery had the distinction of remaining in production there until 1982 when it was closed. Within a short time the brewery was demolished and a housing estate built with Leney Road and Phoenix Drive recalling the names of the past brewing industry. The last local initiative was taken by The Wateringbury Hotel who secured the great weathervane from the brewery tower and allowed it to continue to overlook Wateringbury from their rooftop.

The Leney family also developed an extensive business in East Kent, for in 1859 Alfred Leney of Wateringbury bought the Phoenix Brewery at Dover and traded as Alfred Leney and Co. Ltd. They took over the Castle Brewery and the Diamond Brewery in Dover and in Folkestone the Gun brewery, and in Canterbury the St. Dunstans Brewery. The whole eventually became part of Fremlins.

But the Wateringbury story has more underlying strands, because in 1833 James Fremlin Miller at Wardens Mill married Anne Jude, sister of John Beale Jude the brewer, and their first son Ralph Fremlin learned the brewing business in his uncle's Kent brewery where at the age of seventeen he was working as assistant brewer's clerk.[18] It was good training because he acted as his own accountant when he made his historic mark on Maidstone in 1861 brewing on a derelict brewery site in Earl Street. That brewery was to develop into a major Kent industry. Fremlin's success lay in his idea of being a family brewer, delivering beer direct to his customers at home, because as a very religious man he shunned public houses. Misses Catherine and Mary Thomson of Snodland who knew the family well said that every worker at the brewery was given a Bible. Joined in time by his younger brothers the firm bought many of the older Kent breweries – Canterbury Brewery Company (George Street,) the Beer and Rigden, Faversham, (Court Street), the Lower Brewery, Maidstone, (Stone Street/Gabriels Hill) and the Phoenix Brewery at Dover.

When Fremlins joined the Whitbread organisation in 1967 a strange twist of history occurred in that the company returned to the Phoenix Brewery in whose shadow their founder had been born. The Fremlin name remains on the cottages given to the parishes of Nettlestead and Wateringbury by Frances and Helen in memory of their brother Richard Fremlin, who died in 1916. They were younger sisters and brother of Ralph the brewer.

Fremlins' Earl Street site stopped brewing in 1972 and Faversham is to close in 1990, being the penultimate of the old Kent breweries.

With a few exceptions the great brewery buildings have disappeared from the scene but mention should be made of the strenuous efforts of Hadlow village to retain their redundant brewery as a piece of their village history and after a long period of negotiation the towering building has been converted into housing preserving at the same time the visual outline of their old industry.

Developed from a much older business the secret of its success was again the water supply. When the company of Kenward and Court was formed in 1888 the syllabus claims

> 'an inexhaustive supply of well water. . . peculiarly adapted for the brewing of choice stock and pale ales, which for brilliancy and keeping qualities are well known and compare well with Burton Products.'

The merger policy has had such a great effect that the traditional brewing industry, with but one exception, does now take place in the towns and villages of Kent.

The one proud exception is Shepherd Neame of Faversham. Their brewery has been brewing continuously since 1698 – longer than any other brewery in Britain. Their original site had been selected for the exceptional purity of the water supply, and today it is still drawn from the same source via an artesian well with a 200 foot borehole.

The business founded by Richard Marsh, Mayor of Faversham, remained in his family until it was purchased by Samuel Shepherd in 1741 and when Percy Neame became a partner in 1869 the firm took on its famous name. Mr. Neame became the sole owner in 1877 on the death of his partner Henry Shepherd, the Younger. He bought many freehold properties assuring an output through the firms' own licensed houses. It was a policy which the firm has continued and today they have a tied estate of 264 houses all selling real ale brewed from East Kent hops. They also have a free trade of 700 outlets in Essex and London as well as Kent. Their strength lies not just in their famous traditional brews and their newer successful fashionable lagers but in the family determination to remain independent brewers.

Richard Marsh could not foresee his place in what was to become an historic business so it is interesting to record a new line of Kentish brewers and wonder what their future will be in the history of brewing.

After the famous Maidstone breweries had been closed Philip and Deborah Goacher brought brewing back to Maidstone in 1983 when they established themselves as independent brewers at the Bockingford Brewery. Recently moved to shining new premises Goachers brew 21 barrels of traditional real ale per week using premium malt and the finest Kentish hops. Their Maidstone Ales have in a short time become much appreciated in local free houses.

Larkins Brewery, recently moved to the owners farm at Chiddingstone, has a long association with hops because the family have grown them in Kent since Tudor times. Those grown by the present farmer are used in their brewery where they brew three beers to supply 60 free houses in the south east.

Because the process of brewing relies on the reaction of organic materials on each other the art has remained unchanged for centuries in spite of increased commercial production and more sophisticated equipment – that is until recent years when unnatural processes have been introduced to the detriment of the product.

There are six stages in brewing – grinding, mashing, boiling, cooling, fermenting and racking. The malt is first cleaned and crushed in a mill; the ground malt, now called grist is then mixed with hot water (liquor) in a vessel called a mash tun and allowed to stand while the natural sugars in the malt dissolve into the liquid; this is the process called mashing. After mashing, the liquid which is now called wort, is run off through the slotted base of the vessel. The remaining grains are sprinkled with more hot liquor to remove any last remaining sugars, which is known as sparging. The wort is then run into coppers where it is boiled for an hour or so with hops which adds bitterness and aroma to the sweet mixture. The hopped wort flows from the copper into a vessel called a hop back which also has a slotted base and the liquid runs out of the vessel over a bed of spent hops. Hopped wort is then passed over coolers, which is necessary to prepare the wort for fermenting, after which it is dropped into fermenting vessels and mixed with yeast. Fermentation, the process by which yeast turns sugar into alcohol and carbon dioxide is allowed to proceed for five or six days during which the head of yeast develops on the wort and is skimmed off the surface. At the end of the period the yeast sinks to the bottom of the vessel. When fermentation has finished the green beer is run off into tanks for a few days. The remaining yeast continues to turn the residual sugars into alcohol and also helps to purge the beer of the rough after tastes created by fermentation. Some brewers add extra sugar at this stage to encourage continuing fermentation. Caramel is sometimes added to give a darker colour. Finings, which is a glutinous substance made from the bladder of the sturgeon, is added at the conditioning stage or when the beer is in the cask to fine or clear the beer. The finings attract yeast and other particles and begin to drag them to the bottom of the tank. At the end of fermentation the product which is now beer, is run off into casks or storage tanks with the addition of a little sugar to encourage secondary fermentation in the cask, and a handful of dried hops to give aroma.

Provided that the finished beer is left to brew naturally the result is the traditional draught beer known in the industry as 'cask conditioned beer' or real ale. But that is the point where the unnatural processes have been introduced – instead of secondary fermentation in the cask the process of brewing is terminated. It is conditioned for a short time in tanks under a heavy blanket of carbon dioxide after which it is chilled and filtered to remove the remaining yeast. Next it is pasteurised (heated) to ensure that the termination has been completed. As the natural brewing process has been halted the beer cannot generate its own carbon dioxide and it would be flat and lifeless if served in this condition. It is therefore connected to cylinders of carbon dioxide in the pub cellar which force the gas into the beer when the tap on the bar is operated. These beers are known as keg beers because they are kept in sealed and pressurised containers called kegs.

The same process has been applied to lager. All the main brands of European and Australian lager on sale in Britain are brewed here in spite of advertisements which tend to suggest that they are imported. The aim is to produce beers quickly, which because they are sterile and have a long shelf-life are very profitable. It is estimated that keg beer is twice as profitable as cask beer and keg lager four times as profitable.

Keg beers have been successful because the customer has had no other choice as a result of the Big Six closing local breweries and dominating the market with their own products. But in 1971 a small group of people who were appalled at the way keg beer threatened to replace the traditonal English beers started the Campaign for Real Ale, (CAMRA). It was immediately successful and by the end of the decade had 30,000 members. Among other activities, they held demonstrations, gained media support and produced the Good Beer Guide which lists those pubs which still sell real ale. They were so successful that the brewers responded to the demand for cask conditioned beer. CAMRA also wrote reports on the brewing industry drawing attention to the monopoly grip of the Big Six and the resultant lack of choice for consumers.

The monopoly came to the attention of the Mergers and Monopolies Commission which after a two and a half year investigation published in 1989 their report into the Supply of Beer. The report concluded that – the big brewers dominate the market using their tied estates and their control of the so-called free trade to exploit the customer. Genuine competition is limited and often non-existent. Regional variations in beer prices are not justified. Lager is grossly overpriced, costing the same as beer to produce, but sold for 10p a pint more. New brewers cannot enter the market. Tenants do not have enough security. Unless the government acts, the beer market will become increasingly dominated by a small number of companies.

The plans put forward by the Commission offered more choice, more competition and a more open market for the smaller brewer, namely – that the tenants of national brewers will be able to stock a cask-conditioned guest ale bought from someone other than his brewery on his own terms; that there should be some limitations on the loan tie, by which apparently 'free houses' take a loan from a brewery in return for agreeing to buy their beers; that tenants should get some basic legal security; that independent brewers would be left strictly alone. But most radical is the requirement that national brewers will have to free from the tie half of all pubs they own over the 2,000 limit. This will create several thousand more free houses.

The Commissioner's report has been met with apprehension by both the brewing and the hop industries.

The brewers may have been affected when their monopoly was broken by the Beer Act of 1830, and the structure of the industry may have been fundamentally changed by the mergers and takeovers policy culminating in the 1960s but never before have they been so basically challenged by such sweeping changes to the extent that they must reorganise the whole industry.

The remaining 250 English hop growers now farming a mere 7,000 acres of hops fear that the industry may become too small to be viable and that many of them could be driven out of business. They fear that the biggest brewers may sell off their breweries rather than meet the ceiling of 2,000 tied houses for each brewery. That would allow the entrance of foreign brewers who may choose to buy their hops from their traditional suppliers. Moreover there is a glut of world hops which has a depressant effect on the English market and the English farmer can scarcely compete with imported Chinese hops which are produced with a labour cost of 10p an hour. They feel that the carefully guarded quality of English hops is being disregarded and that the quality of imported hops could be questionable because as they arrive in processed pellet form the quality cannot be checked and the customer could be consuming an inferior product. Moreover making a guest beer compulsory in tied public houses could boost the leading brands at the expense of regional and other small brewers who are proud of their loyalty to English hops.

The brewers have until 1992 to think out new policies. The hop growers are, as in centuries past, dependent on the market. The great paying public can however indicate their preferences by voicing their opinion and by discriminating purchase.

Acknowledgments

Much of the material used is from previously unpublished sources. Thanks are due to Mr. D.L. Nissim, farm manager of Whitbread Hop Farm, Paddock Wood (1980-1985) for permission to use papers at the hop farm. These include the rich sources of the monthly farm reports sent to the brewery by the farm manager 1920-1945, many letters sent out from the farm and many received by the farm, all innocently unaware that in a short time they would be social history. Other rich sources were papers of the Drapers' Company who administered Beltring Farm for 347 years, and those of the Franciscan Friars who allowed me the privilege of being the only lay person to see their Mission to Hoppers records. Similar permission has also been given by the Public Record Office for the papers of E.A. White and Company, and Mr. Nigel Yates for documents in the West Kent Archives Office.

The Campaign for Real Ale; Mr. M. Lander of English Hops Ltd; Shepherd Neame, Faversham; Mr. E.R. Green (Gravesend); Mr. S. Thompson (Wateringbury); Mrs. Y. Shadbolt (Wateringbury); Mr. A. Redsell of the National Hop Growers Association.

Bibliography
> Bickerdyke, J. *The Curiosities of Ale and Beer.* 1889.
> > Reprinted Spring Books, 1965.
> Clark, P. *The English Ale House – A Social History 1200-1830.* Longman, 1983.
> Dunn. M. *Real Draught Beer.* Penguin, 1979.
> Mathias, P. *The Brewing Industry in England,* 1700-1830.
> > Cambridge University Press, 1959.
> Parker, H.H. *The Hop Industry.* 1934.

References

1.   West Kent Archives Office. U 1823/2. F6.

2.   WKA U838. T 577.

3.   Personal Papers. Hop Tithe Records.

4.   Records of the Franciscan Mission to Catholic Hop Pickers.

5.   WKA C/A 11/33 1907.

6.   Public Record Office. Probate Records. Samuel White 1837 and Lawrence Starnes 1843.

7.   Marlborough College Records.

8.   Lord Harris. The History of Kent County Cricket.

9.   The Drapers' Company Papers. H 70.

10.   PRO. BT.31. 15388. Records of Defunct Companies.

11.   Ibid.

12.   WKA. U 1571. The Estate of Mary White.

13.   PRO. BT3. as above.

14.   Whitbread. Beltring Farm Papers et passim.

15.   WKA. U47/17 T 80.

16.   WKA. U 1094. P103.

17.   Census Records. Wateringbury and Hollingbourne.

18.   Census Records. Wateringbury.

19.   WKA. U 442 B14/2.

Index

98